STARVING BABIES

KALEB VALDEZ, DC

Disclaimer: The information contained in this publication, including the audiobook and eBook versions and their associated website(s) are the sole work and opinions of Kaleb Valdez, DC except where otherwise noted. Specific sources and articles cited remain the work and opinions of their respective author(s), who retain copyright as marked.

All information presented in this work is not intended to replace the competent care of a qualified health care professional and is not to be construed as personal medical advice. It is a sharing of knowledge and dissemination of information from the research and experience of Dr. Valdez. He encourages you to make your own health care decisions based upon personal research, in consultation with a qualified health care professional.

If you are pregnant, nursing, taking medication, or have a medical condition, consult your prescribing and primary care provider before discontinuing, using, or changing prescription medication based on this content.

AUTHOR'S NOTE

This book is set in an evolving arena of conflicting data, of contradictory reports and claims. Current events change daily. While some stories help to illustrate historical examples or current issues, these can change and evolve as more information comes to light. Every effort has been made to remain true to the sources cited, but the research and data is as reliable as the people and methods that produce it, including the author of this work. This shouldn't be allowed to eclipse the overall narrative.

The dialogue set forth in this book attempts to stay politically neutral. Sadly, however, politics have come to shape so much of the current discussion. The language in this book is intentionally matched to the body of international research. It diverges from some more politically correct and in-vogue terminology. This is not to exclude any group of the LGBTQ+ or any other community. It is simply to discuss core concepts in a way that reflects the current literature on the world stage. This uses gendered terms like "mother" and "breastfeeding" in connection with pregnancy, rather than alternatives. This use of conventional language is not intended to be exclusionary or marginalize any person or group. Medical and technical terms are often listed in *Italics* throughout and may be included in the glossary at the end.

It also acknowledges that not every birth story is ideal. Some mothers face unplanned single motherhood, infertility challenges, and medical complications. This book begins and ends with a total release of judgment and coercion and asks that the same courtesy pervade the birth community. Birth and motherhood can be a universally unifying force against all that seeks to divide us. There are plenty of challenges facing new and experienced mothers, and guilt and shame should be two of the easiest to relinquish.

ACKNOWLEDGMENTS

The author wishes to thank the following individuals for their input, influence, and oversight in Starving Babies: Kyle Call, Ronda Samuelson, Dr. Cathy Lemon, Sarah Mack, Elisha Roden, Marsha Pettit, Dr. Phillip and Whitney Guison, Kimberly Vlassis, Alex Dobson, Amanda and Scarlett Merchant, Katie Dean, Laura David, Candace Owens, James Biesert, Janis Wilson, Barbara Payne, Debbie Hart, Destiny Best, Lisa Burden, Fr. David and Esther Lubliner, Rani, Sama, and Hamroosh Alabed, Nada Nasser, Lowell and Angie Nash, Alfredo and Whitney Lopez, Kimber Nielsen, Destiny Yarbro, Diane Dean, and Ethan Johnson. Thank you to my partner in practice and life coach, Sir-Doctor-Captain Bridger Cutler. Special thanks to Kelly Allen, Adrienne and Gary Weiss, Ken Raines, and the late Dr. William Neal for nurturing my love of writing.

And to the many patients and providers who have furthered my practice of the art of chiropractic and have demonstrated loving service as their first technique. To the many mentors, instructors, professors, and birth workers I've been blessed to work with: Dr. Elias Osuna, Drs. Jonathan and Taylor Kouts, Michael Fernandez, Dr. Bruce Bishop, Dr. Andrew Hatch, Dr. Anjum Odwani, Dr. Vanessa Morales, Dr. William Morgan, Dr. Gene Giggleman, Dr. J. Michael Perryman, Dr. Hunter Kershen, Dr. Jake Shumann, Drs. Antonio and Nichelle Gurule, Drs. Kemp and Kiana Spencer, Dr. Mayer Green, Dr. Thuy Vi

Nguyen, Dr. Jared and Charlotte Nelson, Dr. Spencer Bruce, Dr. Meng Sun, Dr. Adam Hansen, Dr. Tony Ebel, Dr. Hugh Hunger, Dr. Natalie Rosenzweig, and Dr. Mark Charrette. To my dear friends Megan and Brandon Ayers, Nick and Ashley Bramwell, Aaron and Gabby Martinez, Mustapha El Akkari and Dima Machnouk, Lavor and Karen Fox, for your constant loving support. And to Duane Cutler for encouraging this book into existence. Thank you to my family for all the feedback and love, especially to Connie Keith and Kelly Allen for being the best mothers on the planet.

TABLE OF CONTENTS

For those who have found the courage to say "No",

to those who are now waking up and joining us.

Welcome to the Brave New World.

And for my best friend, BT.

ONE:
THE FORMULA CRISIS:
PROFILE OF THE PROBLEM

A WHISTLEBLOWER REPORT

At the beginning of the formula crisis, in late April and May 2022, mothers all over the United States set off each morning, searching for the next source of formula for their newborns. It was a heartbreaking scene. Many of these women were residents of the inner city, minority mothers, many with jobs, often single and traveling on foot or by public transportation. They were often forced to leave their children with a caretaker, but some had their babies in tow as they visited their usual stores only to be greeted by empty shelves. They spoke with sympathetic but helpless employees who rechecked their stock, hoping for a delivery they had overlooked or a late arrival of formula. These mothers trudged on, moving from store to store. Some faced a two-hour bus ride to find the prized formula. Unfortunately, due to rationing at these rare locations with supply, their purchases were limited. They would make the trek all too soon again to restock. The scene was similar across twenty-six states that reported out of stock rates higher than 40%[1].

1   BBC. (2022, May 9). *US faces Baby Formula 'crisis' as shortage worsens.* BBC News. Retrieved August 10, 2022, from https://www.bbc.com/news/business-61387183

The origin of this crisis started in the final months of 2021. A whistleblower report[2] came to light claiming Abbott Nutrition's facility in Sturgis, Michigan was facing serious problems with the cleanliness of their facility and the integrity of their products. These included Similac, Alimentum, and EleCare. The person making the report also raised doubts about some of the past behaviors of the company. He stated they had concealed certain issues from Food and Drug Administration inspectors in previous visits. The earliest reports of this nature began in September of 2021 and continued until February 2022.[3]

This latest whistleblower made some stunning allegations based on what he observed. In a place like Sturgis, Michigan, Abbott Nutrition is one of the largest employers. Making a report like this could seriously jeopardize this man's livelihood. If the company chose to retaliate, he would be forced to change careers or move. The report describes his employment history at Abbott before these claims as "stellar." He even received awards for his great job performance. This was not some angry employee looking to burn bridges on his way out the door, but someone who cared enough about his job to put in extra effort. This is someone who was once proud of where he worked.

According to his statement, Abbott had falsified records. Sometimes they skipped over test results on products before shipping them. They flubbed maintenance records. He alleges that Abbott even failed to recall product after learning it tested positive for bacteria in the formula powder, called a *nonconformity*. During the 2019 audit by the FDA, the report states "active efforts were undertaken and even celebrated" to keep the FDA unaware of these nonconformities. The

2   *CONFIDENTIAL DISCLOSURE RE ABBOTT LABORATORIES' PRODUCTION SITE IN STURGIS, MICHIGAN.* DocumentCloud. (2021, October 19). Retrieved August 10, 2022, from https://www.documentcloud.org/documents/22051317-confidential-disclosure-re-abbott-laboratories-production-site-in-sturgis-michigan

3   Knight, S. (2022, May 17). *Company responsible for Tainted Baby Formula Has Monopoly Over Aid Program sales.* Company Responsible for Tainted Baby Formula Has Monopoly Over Aid Program Sales. Retrieved August 10, 2022, from https://truthout.org/articles/company-responsible-for-tainted-baby-formula-has-monopoly-over-aid-program-sales/

report also claimed that since the labeling system failed often, some product was impossible to trace or recall. Staff was often unsure if a particular batch had been retrieved after testing positive due to this problem.

Some of his allegations are very technical and specific to the manufacturing industry. Some are obvious failures to take common sense steps to ensure a clean, germ-free environment. Such a nutrient-dense product like infant formula is a magnet for bacteria. It's meant to easily break down for digestion. It's intended to support healthy bacteria in the baby's tummy, not invasive germs in the formula can. This makes it that much more important for the factory to maintain clean standards. Once contaminated, especially with certain types of bacteria, the product becomes a breeding ground for germs.

One of the most alarming assertions from this whistleblower report was about the equipment conditions, which could breed and spread bacterial contaminants. These could potentially infect consumers, especially those with weakened or inexperienced immune systems, premature babies, or other medically vulnerable individuals. These babies rely on formula as the core source of their nutrition. Without mother's antibodies to protect this rich supply, the constituents in formula are free for the taking to whatever microbe gets there first. The report says that while there are many violations across multiple categories, "The common thread was and is to conceal the reality of what is taking place at the Sturgis site. The violations are neither inadvertent nor minor in nature."[4]

Back in 2019, Abbott faced an inspection of Calcilo XD due to discolored and rancid-smelling formula. This is the natural result

---

4   *CONFIDENTIAL DISCLOSURE RE ABBOTT LABORATORIES' PRODUCTION SITE IN STURGIS, MICHIGAN.* DocumentCloud. (2021, October 19). Retrieved August 10, 2022, from https://www. documentcloud.org/documents/22051317-confidential-disclosure-re-abbott-laboratories-production-site-in-sturgis-michigan

of bacterial activity, outside air, and moisture seeping into formula powder. The company issued a recall after a significant portion of multiple batches showed this problem[5]. The investigation showed this was due to something they call seam failure. Sometimes powder gets stuck between the lid of the can and the foil sticker seal, preventing airtight sealing[6]. Abbott reported back that they had increased their frequency of "seam checks." Such action should have corrected the issue, so the problem was considered solved.

However, the October 2021 whistleblower report shed light on how the factory was passing these seam checks. It wasn't through improving their process. The checks were being performed on empty cans, which is an obvious way to show no formula on the seams. This was a likely reason for the relapse of "seam integrity" issues that was reported again, starting in August of 2020. This time instead of affecting Calcilo XD, it was for Similac Sensitive. Half of the poorly sealed formula was on site in Sturgis, but the other half had already been shipped. Management heard, but this time no recall was ever issued, the report states.

Before the discovery of the Similac seams, another breakdown occurred a month before, in July 2020. Certain test results for nine batches of product were missing. For each batch, three different chemists and one auditor approved the missing test results. The whistleblower states "In essence, the certifications as to the test results were patently false as the test results were not included."

This would signal a major flaw in the production and quality check process for testing these batches. Again, when management became

5   Center for Food Safety and Applied Nutrition. (2019, September 17). *Abbott Laboratories recalls Calcilo XD® infant formula*. U.S. Food and Drug Administration. Retrieved August 10, 2022, from https://www.fda.gov/safety/recalls-market-withdrawals-safety-alerts/abbott-laboratories-recalls-calcilo-xdr-infant-formula

6   Beach, C. (2022, April 28). *Former employee blows whistle on Baby Formula Production Plant tied to outbreak*. Food Safety News. Retrieved August 10, 2022, from https://www.foodsafetynews.com/2022/04/former-employee-blows-whistle-on-baby-formula-production-plant-tied-to-outbreak/

aware, they took no noticeable corrective action. Out of these nine batches, there were a documented thirty-six performance errors. This suggests a serious pattern of disregard for the factory's own internal checks and balances to ensure safety and reliability of their products. The report concludes that "Signing off on projection pages with missing test results was repeated multiple times. This was neither inadvertent nor isolated."

These are serious errors. Based on these examples, a view of the culture of the leadership at Abbott begins to emerge. And it isn't very reassuring. At the Sturgis plant and elsewhere, this behavior shows a general attitude of disregard for oversight. It's disdain for the system designed to protect American babies. These corporations hire communication experts and lawyers to make statements to deflect investigations away from reports like this one. Irresponsible actions like these can endanger the health of newborns.

At the Sturgis factory, they called these contaminated batches "the micro batches." This refers to the batches with microbial contaminants. They were a major source of stress, apparently, for some of the quality assurance team at Sturgis during the 2019 audit by the FDA. One member of management was reported to have been warning some of the staff, alerting them that the FDA "was on the 'right trail'. She volunteered that she was amazed the FDA was unable to discover what occurred with the micro batches." The whistleblower claims that in one meeting, a senior official discussed "the awkwardness of having to avoid providing direct answers to questions asked by the FDA." The report is unclear on the exact nature of what was withheld, but it is evident that there was "a conscious effort to avoid disclosure."[7]

---

7   *CONFIDENTIAL DISCLOSURE RE ABBOTT LABORATORIES' PRODUCTION SITE IN STURGIS, MICHIGAN.* DocumentCloud. (2021, October 19). Retrieved August 10, 2022, from https://www.documentcloud.org/documents/22051317-confidential-disclosure-re-abbott-laboratories-production-site-in-sturgis-michigan

This is the infuriating reality of such a bloated government agency like the FDA, which seems content to go through the motions of audit and oversight, while the corporations out-maneuver the inspectors and in their words, "avoid disclosure." The micro batches of 2019 are just one example. Those parents and pediatricians who are paying attention to Abbott's track record are rightfully frustrated with the manufacturer for such gross breaches of their duty. In the face of this incompetence, the FDA stands and lectures parents on the risks of contaminated formula.

"The FDA does not recommend that parents and caregivers make infant formulas at home because of serious health and safety concerns," it states. "The potential problems with homemade formulas include contamination... These problems are very serious, and the consequences range from severe nutritional imbalances to foodborne illnesses, both of which can be life-threatening."[8]

This warning would bear much more weight if the FDA were not addressing such frequent or ongoing reports of contaminated batches at places like Sturgis. They presume to lecture mothers on bacterial contamination while they deal with yet another maintenance failure or another audit. These giant companies are the producers the government agency says it regulates vigilantly. Both sides claim to be so committed to the purity of the infant formula, the accuracy of their labels, and the integrity of their cans' seals. Parents want to trust product manufacturers with safety and efficacy of powdered infant formula. But after observing Abbott's reported deception and the FDA's inaction and incompetence, they've lost the confidence of most of those who are paying attention.

---

8   Center for Food Safety and Applied Nutrition. (2021, February 24). *FDA advises parents and caregivers to not make or feed homemade infant.* U.S. Food and Drug Administration. Retrieved August 10, 2022, from https://www.fda.gov/food/alerts-advisories-safety-information/fda-advises-parents-and-caregivers-not-make-or-feed-homemade-infant-formula-infants

Abbott Nutrition's parent company, Abbott Laboratories, has a criminal history. More than a decade ago, in May 2012, Abbott Laboratories entered an agreement with the Office of Inspector General of the Department of Health and Human Services[9]. It was discovered that from 1998 to 2006, they had marketed a drug off-label to treat schizophrenia with no FDA approval to do so. They negotiated the guilty plea to a single misdemeanor charge. The settlement was part of a larger plea agreement, which fined them $1.5 billion and required five years of probation. While this agreement did not pertain to Abbott Nutrition specifically, the principles of disclosure and transparency apply. It was a glimpse into how this and other giant corporations tend to operate when national attention is directed elsewhere. Only when a bright and uncomfortable light is shown on their deceptive actions are they called to account. Their vast legal resources help them lessen or avoid consequences, and their willingness to pay large amounts of money helps to cool tempers in Washington. They can justify the cost of these fines as part of doing business, if enforcement ever does catch up with them. They promise publicly to change, to abide by the rules. This time, they say, they really mean it. But after having a decade in which to make cultural and procedural changes, they end up back in the same situation. Little seems to have changed in the intervening decades.

DELAYED RESPONSE

Back to the present, the latest whistleblower came forward in October of 2021, yet the FDA took no substantive action until the following year. It wasn't until the end of February 2022, five months after these claims surfaced, that inspectors arrived in Sturgis[10]. They now had four or

---

9   Abbott Laboratories Sentenced for Misbranding Drug. (2012, October 2). *JUSTICE NEWS*. Retrieved August 10, 2022, from https://www.justice.gov/opa/pr/abbott-laboratories-sentenced-misbranding-drug.

10   Burdick, S. (2022, May 16). *White House takes steps to ease infant formula shortage but fails to*

five very sick babies in the investigation, three reported through FDA complaints and one from a CDC case finding. The complaints said they had been fed formula from the Sturgis factory. Tragically, two of these infants passed away with infections shortly after they were diagnosed. The FDA inspectors did walk-through inspections and lab testing the first two days in February. What they found made them concerned enough to recommend halting production at the Sturgis factory. They ordered Abbott to make repairs and perform the necessary cleaning before reopening.

In their report, the FDA told Abbott "You did not establish a system of process controls covering all stages of processing that was designed to ensure that infant formula does not become adulterated due to the presence of microorganisms in the formula or in the processing environment."[11]

One of the places within the factory that tested positive for bacteria was the machine that feeds plastic scoops into the formula cans. This is a high care area, given its close contact with the formula itself. Here the inspectors also noticed duct tape on the floor with debris above and below it that tested positive for bacteria. There was water dripping onto the floor throughout the facility, and in total, they documented 310 "water events." These include leaks, moisture, and condensation in dry powdered formula production areas. The dryers in these areas have a history of deterioration that goes back at least as far as September of 2018. Inspection reports from August 2021 show six cracks and pits in the main chamber of one dryer. They found six more in the main chamber of another. Ten cracked braces were noted in another dryer.

These equipment breakdowns increase the possibility of bacterial contamination. It's tempting to explain away these findings. Maybe

---

address industry monopoly. Children's Health Defense. Retrieved August 10, 2022, from https://childrenshealthdefense.org/defender/baby-formula-shortage-white-house/

11   Food and Drug Administration, & Hathaway, T. J., Form FDA 4831–9 (n.d.). Inspectional Observations.

the company just fell on hard times. Maybe during the shutdowns associated with pandemic measures, they were unable to afford repairs or improvements to their plant equipment. These issues, however, continued for four years. While Abbott waded through FDA red tape and failed inspection paperwork, they were busy buying back $5.73 billion of their own stock.[12] Their financial reports showed that they also issued a hefty bonus to their executives and shareholders. This money could have gone to repair their production lines. It could have created backup systems to put more eggs in more baskets. Instead, the current system allowed the profit-hungry foxes to guard the henhouse.

After the FDA conducted their inspection on the first two days of February 2022, on February 17th, they issued an advisory alert to "avoid purchasing or using certain powdered infant formula produced in the Sturgis, MI facility."[13] Three weeks after that inspection, Abbott finally issued their voluntary recall.[14] The term *voluntary* suggests an image of concerned, principled scientists watching out for babies' safety. It calls to mind a company that wants to do the right thing if there's even a slight chance their product is bad. The sinister claims this report makes is that Abbott may not have issued the recall if they hadn't been caught. They'd gotten away with it before. Abbott's group of executives were willing to pay themselves and buy back their own stock instead of repair their factory. They hired managers and leaders who actively worked to "avoid disclosure" to the government agency in charge of inspecting their systems. And they have done this all

12   *Abbott Laboratories Stock Buybacks.* Abbott Laboratories Stock Buybacks (Quarterly). (n.d.). Retrieved August 10, 2022, from https://ycharts.com/companies/ABT/stock_buyback

13   FDA. (n.d.). *FDA warns consumers not to use certain powdered infant formula produced in Abbott Nutrition's facility in Sturgis, Michigan.* U.S. Food and Drug Administration. Retrieved August 10, 2022, from https://www.fda.gov/news-events/press-announcements/fda-warns-consumers-not-use-certain-powdered-infant-formula-produced-abbott-nutritions-facility

14   ABBOTT VOLUNTARILY RECALLS POWDER FORMULAS MANUFACTURED AT ONE PLANT. (2022, February 17). *Abbott Mediaroom.* Retrieved August 10, 2022, from https://abbott.mediaroom.com/2022-02-17-Abbott-Voluntarily-Recalls-Powder-Formulas-Manufactured-at-One-Plant.

before. This makes both sides look bad. The agency that is supposed to be savvy to these problems wasn't aware of them until babies started getting sick. It highlighted the negligence of their inspectors, and the failures to monitor the current production.

The American public is expected to trust that the Food and Drug Administration understands the complex world of infant formula manufacturing. Congress allocates tax dollars to this agency for this very purpose. The FDA requires companies to receive their approval before making and selling infant formula, because their oversight is so important for public safety. The bar is set so high that so far, only a few companies have been willing to clear it. Occasionally private organizations step in to address the growing crises of contamination and distrust. It's time for the public to step back and ask themselves if these regulatory agencies merit such trust. The other enforcement tasks that Congress has assigned to this agency do not instill much confidence. This is the administrative arm of government at its most incompetent. Is the FDA still the true standard of safety and efficacy they hold themselves out to be? Do parents really trust these companies and agencies? Or do they toss a can of baby formula into the cart at Walmart and hurry home to a hungry infant without a second thought?

The public is beginning to wake up to Abbott's history of infractions leading up to the current closure. Seeing the molasses-like speed with which the FDA responded to credible concerns, are they really protecting babies from bad formula? Given the pace at which the factory closure happened, can these corporations or government agencies truly claim to have the best interest of their customers and taxpayers at heart? Do they put public interests and safety first? Their actions suggest that their motives may not align with their claims. By the end of February, one additional infection case was confirmed in an infant with exposure to Sturgis formula. The suspected culprit in all these cases was *Cronobacter sakazakii*.

PROFILE OF THE PATHOGEN

Cronobacter refers to the genus of the bacterial species, which is like a last name for a specific family with multiple members. Since this type of bacteria usually attacks the gut, it was formerly known as *Enterobacter*, "entero" referring to the intestines. In 2007, the name was changed to "*Cronobacter*."[15] This is a morbid tribute to Cronos, the Greek demigod who devoured babies. This pathogen can be fatal, specifically to babies with weakened immune systems or who are still developing, like premature newborns. Infections usually occur after the bacteria in formula mixes with water in the formula and is bottle-fed to the baby. The germ's native environment hasn't been determined yet, because it is almost exclusively found in infant formula powder. Since the species builds a wax caste around itself, it is capable of surviving for long periods of time in dry environments. Cans of infant formula are ideal for it to culture in and to hibernate.

Many times, it also appears alongside Salmonella strains. Salmonella is another common hitchhiker on equipment and ingredients used for infant formula. As mentioned, powdered formula is intentionally nutrient rich. It is readily absorbed and digested and packed with the simple sugars and vitamins that bacteria love. Infant formula is different from breastmilk in many ways. Breastmilk includes its own army of white blood cells like security guards, to prevent bacteria from taking over the nutrients. Infant formula is missing this protection, which presents an ongoing challenge for formula manufacturers.

---

15   Iversen, C., Mullane, N., McCardell, B., Tall, B. D., Lehner, A., Fanning, S., Stephan, R., & Joosten, H. (2008, June 1). *Cronobacter gen. nov., a new genus to accommodate the biogroups of Enterobacter sakazakii...* International Journal of Systematic and Evolutionary Microbiology. Retrieved August 10, 2022, from https://doi.org/10.1099%2Fijs.0.65577-0

How big of a threat is the *Cronobacter* outbreak? It's difficult to find a number, since *Cronobacter* infections are not nationally reported. Infections can be serious, since it often attacks the central nervous system and bloodstream. Since infants have stomachs designed to absorb breastmilk, they are less acidic than adult stomachs, which may be one reason the bacteria can survive and spread in newborn stomachs. Research has shown that the median age of most infections was just two days old, and that 94% of cases occur in babies less than 28 days old[16]. There has also been no evidence for infant-to-infant transmission of the disease. In the documented cases, babies had all been fed contaminated formula[17]. This infection is very rare, and since 1958, there have been just 120 reported cases of *Cronobacter* infections, about three cases per year worldwide[18] as of 2009.

Our enforcement systems exist to hold formula manufacturers to high standards of cleanliness. Their product is going to a vulnerable population. When *Salmonella* or *Cronobacter* outbreaks occur, manufacturers need to treat them seriously. But when a federal agency and a company behave as the FDA and Abbott have, it's hard to take their warnings seriously regarding the risks of contaminating baby food supply at home.

It is even harder to justify fearmongering and the gaslighting of parents, who are so programmed to fear this infection. Parents are held hostage by this fear as they seek to address far more pressing formula shortage issues. They should feel empowered to explore forgotten methods of feeding their babies at home when large hubs like the one in Sturgis are shut down and formula is scarce. Considering all

---

16   Iversen, C., A. Lehner, N. Mullane, E. Bidlas, I. Cleenwerck, J. Marugg, S. Fanning, R. Stephan, and H. Joosten. 2007. "The taxonomy of Enterobacter sakazakii: proposal of a new genus Cronobacter", 1. BMC Evol. Biol. 7:64.

17   FAO/WHO [Food and Agriculture Organization of the United Nations/World Health Organization]. 2008. Enterobacter sakazakii (Cronobacter spp.) in powdered follow-up formulae. Microbiological Risk Assessment Series No. 15. Rome. 90pp.

18   Centers for Disease Control and Prevention (CDC). Cronobacter species isolation in two infants - New Mexico, 2008. MMWR Morb Mortal Wkly Rep. 2009 Oct 30;58(42):1179-83. PMID: 19875980.

the changes the American household has undergone since 1958, the beginning of *Cronobacter* outbreaks, this infection is simply not the major baby-killing demon its name would suggest.

Four major members make up the *Cronobacter* family. *Sakazakii* is the one most often associated with infant formula contamination. In the recent infections used to justify closing the Sturgis plant, the FDA and CDC blamed *Cronobacter sakazakii* for two infant deaths. They were unable to show a direct relation between the infections, though. The bacteria found in the Sturgis factory were not a genetic match for the strain taken from the sick babies. They utilized a testing method called Whole Genome Sequencing to track the genes in the bacteria. This helps identify the source of outbreaks. To date, they say however, "No outbreaks of *Cronobacter* have been detected using [this method]."[19]

This would have been the smoking gun, but Abbott pointed to this lack of evidence in order to deny blame for the fatalities. *Cronobacter* strains did match genes found elsewhere in the homes, including the formula bottles and the distilled water used to mix the formula. (Thoroughly cleaning any baby feeding equipment is so important.)

Once testing proved the germs from the factory didn't match those found in the infected babies, Abbott seemed to heave a sigh of relief. The national media, the FDA, and Abbott all seemed relieved that the infection didn't come from the factory. Almost nobody realized the fact that *Cronobacter* cultures *were* found in the Sturgis factory, along with *Salmonella*. These were the bacteria that the infections were tested against. The fact that these were not present in the tested batches is only a slight reassurance. The single case of *Salmonella*

---

19   Center for Food Safety and Applied Nutrition. (n.d.). *Investigation of Cronobacter infections from powdered infant formula.* U.S. Food and Drug Administration. Retrieved August 10, 2022, from https://www.fda.gov/food/outbreaks-foodborne-illness/fda-investigation-Cronobacter-infections-powdered-infant-formula-february-2022?mc_cid=2dec3cdd26

mentioned in an FDA complaint connected to Sturgis was dropped in early March for a similar lack of a genetic link.[20]

By the end of March, the FDA had completed genetic analysis of the *Cronobacter sakazakii* samples taken from Sturgis. They identified five different strains of bacteria from the factory samples. On March 22, the FDA released the reports of their inspections at Sturgis.[21] These inspection reports are not the final determinations of the agency, simply what they observed. Their notes, though, provide plenty of cause for concern.

NOTHING TO SEE HERE

On May 12, 2022, the CDC announced it was concluding its investigation. The FDA had established an incident management group a month earlier that would make recommendations to prevent this sort of outbreak from reoccurring.

By May 16, Abbott Nutrition and the FDA entered a legal agreement, called a proposed consent decree of permanent injunction[22]. This included three Abbott leaders, who filed it in the United States District Court for the Western District of Michigan. It restated similar agreements that Abbott had previously entered but had failed to uphold. It seemed to include everything that went wrong with the "micro batches incidents." They stated they would test their products for bacteria. They agreed to shut down production and notify the FDA in the event of contamination. They would implement cleaning standards, environmental monitoring, and employee training programs. Maybe this time something would be different.

20   Edney, A. (2022, May 12). Bloomberg.com. Retrieved August 10, 2022, from https://www.bloomberg.com/news/articles/2022-05-12/inspectors-saw-bacteria-risk-at-abbott-formula-factory-last-year

21   Food and Drug Administration, & Hathaway, T. J., Form FDA 4831-9 (n.d.). Inspectional Observations.

22   *Justice Department files complaint and proposed consent decree to ensure safety of Abbott Laboratories' infant formula.* The United States Department of Justice. (2022, May 16). Retrieved August 10, 2022, from https://www.justice.gov/Usao-wdmi/pr/2022_0516_Abbott

Is Abbott the only infant formula manufacturer? Of course not. But it's a very exclusive club, and they are one of the big ones. There aren't many major competitors in this industry. Just three companies make up 98% of all the infant formula sales, and these are the only three companies the US government will do business with: Abbott, Mead Johnson, and Gerber[23]. Abbott has been very much under the public eye during the present crisis. Abbott has the largest market share, and their Sturgis facility is one of their main production hubs.

At the end of May, the House Committee on Energy and Commerce held a meeting in Congress with the FDA and Abbott Nutrition. Both sides received what amounted to a stern talking-to for failing to take appropriate actions leading to the shutdown and ensuing shortage. The President of Abbott North America, Christopher Calamari, attended with two other executives from Reckitt-Benckiser and Gerber Gerber, the makers of Enfamil and Good Start respectively. The FDA sent three officials to represent its interests. The FDA commissioner acknowledged that their response to the reports "was too slow and there were decisions that were suboptimal along the way. Our oversight is critical, but a return to normal will only occur when Abbott takes the steps to resume production in a safe manner."[24] Suboptimal would be a good description for the FDA's actions, based on these reports. How critical was their oversight in this instance? Did they do their job? If not, what prevented them from monitoring and enforcing these agreed upon standards? If Abbott leadership was working to "avoid disclosure", how can the American public trust their oversight?

The FDA claimed they needed more funding. Maybe then they could have stopped this from happening. How much more funding

23   Oliveira, V. (2011, September 11). *Winner takes (almost) all: How WIC affects the infant formula market.* USDA ERS - Infant Formula Market. Retrieved September 8, 2022, from https://www.ers.usda.gov/amber-waves/2011/september/infant-formula-market/

24   Tomey, R. (2022, May 30). *FDA, Abbott Labs both to blame for the ongoing Baby Formula Shortage.* Newstarget.com. Retrieved August 10, 2022, from https://newstarget.com/2022-05-30-fda-abbott-share-blame-baby-formula-shortage.html

did they need? $20 million, they claimed. Surely that would have covered the cost of a plane ticket to Sturgis, and perhaps a rental car for an inspector to visit the factory when the first report came out in October of the previous year. By the time it was brought to a vote, Congress approved an additional $28 million in emergency spending to "bolster [the FDA's] ability to relieve the shortage and prevent future problems."[25] Abbott also established a fund to help alleviate the shortage that resulted in part from their negligence.

To illustrate the depth of the problem, suppose a mother hears the previous account of infant formula contamination. What if she decided she wanted to switch to another supplier? What are her options? How could she do this? Due to the nature of the industry, the way contracts with the government are set up, when Abbott sneezes, the entire infant formula system gets a cold. The shortages lasted for months and constituted a large percentage of the infant formula market.

It's tempting to analyze a failure this large in terms of who is right, and who is wrong. Was this shortage a problem with the greedy manufacturer or ineffective government? Depending on the answer to that question, the logical response is either to increase government power to check the corporations or to argue for less regulation, to make agencies more effective at oversight and encourage free market competition.

The reality, however, after reviewing Congressional testimonies, industry reports, and seeing the official response to this crisis is a bit more complex than one single point of failure. It's possible for both sides to be at fault. We can have bureaucrats making laws that aren't being followed, inspectors being lied to or sidetracked, and executives motivated more by profit than anything else. We can have good

25   Jennifer Shutt, L. I. M. 17. (2022, May 17). *U.S. House to vote on $28 million for FDA to relieve infant formula shortage.* Louisiana Illuminator. Retrieved August 10, 2022, from https://lailluminator.com/2022/05/17/u-s-house-to-vote-on-28-million-for-fda-to-relieve-infant-formula-shortage/

people working in the factory and inside the agency whose hands are tied. And at the top, we have a struggle between a giant company and a power-hungry Congress. More regulations, more funding, and more official oversight may not fix this. Washington can't spend its way out of this problem, and that is very perplexing to politicians who rely almost exclusively on the power of the purse to cure societal ills. It's a great match, however, for executives of companies ready to receive more taxpayer dollars. If they can avoid some costly repairs, buy back some of their shares, and give themselves a large bonus, even better. It's worth a few uncomfortable conversations on Capitol Hill. They can position themselves as the benevolent company with a voluntary recall, a support hotline, and some formula donations to local foodbanks.

There is solid logic in calling for the diversification of the industry, an end to the oligopoly, the rule by a few, that characterizes the infant formula industry. This can be done without completely deregulating the industry. The country also needs to recognize the inefficiencies on the government side and work to address the systemic breakdowns.

This recent episode showcased the cost of inaction. The burden of overregulation and the elimination of competition is not serving consumers. An industry that deals with such a key product needs oversight and transparency. There must also be accountability from the companies entrusted with delivering clean product. They must deliver quality ingredients with the necessary nutritional content. If they want to be the only option, if they've pursued monopolistic policies, they must be able to do so reliably and readily as demand requires. That's the job.

The government appears increasingly uninterested in the latest research. Manufacturers are equally aloof about sourcing the best and cleanest ingredients. And why would they? Those increase the cost of production, reduces their profits. The system protects its own interests, which is increasingly centralized planning of an entire industry. These executives and politicians control a precious, inflexible commodity. They realize they have something their customers will do almost anything to get. Think of the army of mothers riding buses for hours to feed their babies. That is worth a lot of money in the right business model. They've spent a lot of energy setting such a model up, and they won't let it disappear overnight.

The government enjoys the power of selecting the winners and losers. Manufacturers can avoid public scrutiny or the open competition of a free market system. Their biggest profits come from state contracts that have little to do with their consumers.

And if Congress insists on spending more money on an agency that claims to protect babies from contaminated foods, and lectures parents about doing the same, they must produce results. A 2019 study conducted by the Healthy Babies Bright Futures organization tested 168 baby foods. They found that 95% were contaminated with toxic levels of heavy metals. Infant formula was found to be laced with arsenic, lead, cadmium, and mercury, as well as other neurotoxins. It exceeded the FDA's limit of one part per billion in 12 out of the 13 containers tested[26]. Occasionally, someone in the private sector like this foundation steps in to do the FDA's job.

THE NATIONAL SCORECARD FOR HEALTH

These glimpses show the public how pathetic the government's job performance truly is. These are the things they expect their FDA to be testing for and to address with bad actors. But the government seems asleep at the wheel. Money is driving. And infant health nationally

---

26   Houlihan, J., & Brody, C. (2019, October). *What's in my baby's food?* Healthy Babies Bright Futures. Retrieved August 21, 2022, from https://www.healthybabyfood.org/sites/healthybabyfoods.org/files/2019-10/BabyFoodReport_FULLREPORT_ENGLISH_R5b.pdf

is careening over a cliff. The United States is the only country in the world with a rising maternal mortality rate, and it is already one of the highest in high-income countries. They currently rank 33rd out of the 36 countries in the Organization of Economic Cooperation and Development (OECD). Black and Latino mothers and babies are dying at rates more than twice the national average.[27] This is a problem the government is not winning, even as they spend and regulate more. Something is missing from the national conversation. Something other countries seem to inherently grasp.

Discussion among experts in the international community on contaminated and absent formula begins with the recommendation of breastfeeding. The infant formula industry makes a product susceptible to contamination. Bacteria love it as much as babies do. Consuming powdered formula products has an inherent risk because babies don't receive the accompanying immune support that breastmilk includes. This national formula shortage would have been undeniably less devastating, less controlling of public attention if more mothers had the option of breastfeeding their babies. A greater number are beginning to wake up to this reality, however, and attempts to initiate breastfeeding are on the rise.

Reports like the Sturgis whistleblower should shock parents and pediatricians who trust that infants are receiving safe formula. It shows a system that is rotten to its core. Nature has already designed the ultimate system to feed babies and protect them from contaminated food. But the percentage currently receiving the benefits of this natural supply has never been lower. The inability to breastfeed and the reliance on powdered formula is especially rampant in inner cities, in minority and oftentimes single mother households.[28] Parents

27   Cohen, J. (2021, August 1). *U.S. maternal and infant mortality: More signs of public health neglect.* Forbes. Retrieved September 14, 2022, from https://www.forbes.com/sites/joshuacohen/2021/08/01/us-maternal-and-infant-mortality-more-signs-of-public-health-neglect/?sh=1f499223a508
28   Beauregard, J. L., Hamner, H. C., Chen, J., Avila-Rodriguez, W., Elam-Evans, L. D., & Perrine, C. G. (2019, August 29). *Racial disparities in breastfeeding initiation and duration among...* Centers for Disease

must be able to rely on the safety practices like the ones this factory has a record of violating. They should be able to trust programs, inspections, and enforcement to keep them safe, like the ones the FDA failed to deploy until the situation escalated. It was met with a suboptimal agency response, followed immediately by a demand for more spending. The next generation is the most at risk from these breakdowns and shortages. They are paying the price for our dependence on the broken system.

Nobody is coming to save the next generation from the greed that occupies such powerful and profitable positions. Just an army of mothers. For those who do not breastfeed their babies, these formula manufacturers are their only option. And they know it.

There is hope, however. It is possible to make a change. It's not too late. This system has existed for more than a hundred years, so change won't be easy. Improving the current reality requires an understanding of the history behind it. The infant formula giants have been steadily moving towards the profits and power they now enjoy. They always crave more. They are like the mythical titan Cronos, devouring babies. Thankfully the recent tremors that have shaken the national formula have woken many parents to the shortcomings of how America feeds and fortifies newborns. Many families are waking up to the important struggle for health and autonomy, for the power to make their own decisions and to investigate all their options.

The formula shortages are symptoms of far bigger problems beneath the surface of what has become an emotionally charged and polarizing topic. It's more than the occasional bad batch of infant formula, or the inconvenience of empty store shelves. This is something that strikes at the heart of the ability to birth, feed, and raise healthy babies. It is time to address a deep and fundamental starvation that goes even beyond the formula crisis.

Control and Prevention. Retrieved August 10, 2022, from http://dx.doi.org/10.15585/mmwr.mm6834a3

THE LEGEND OF CRONOS

The hero of the Greek legend of Cronos, for whom the infamous bacteria mentioned has been named, is a mother, Rhea, who finally toppled the titan. She fed him a stone. She realized his treachery and rescued her baby from the fate of all the others that had been devoured before. That baby was Zeus, and he grew up and returned as a stranger to face his father. He gave him a bottle of something to drink that made him vomit up his siblings from Cronos's belly. The devoured generation returned and fought a ten-year war against the titan, eventually ending his power.

Today's generation of mothers are waking up, like Rhea. They see that this insatiable giant is separating and profiting from the newborns. The infant formula titan is a $70 billion giant[29], and it is expected to grow to almost $104 billion by 2026[30]. It is devouring and separating babies from mothers almost before birth. While Cronos eats well, and the Cronobacter strains are multiplying and spreading, our babies are not. They are starving.

STARVING BABIES

"Starving" calls to mind a lack of food, or even water, by an older definition. But this is not how it is being used in this book. "To starve", the dictionary tells us, can also mean "to suffer or perish from deprivation."[31] What are we deprived of or withholding from our most vulnerable population? We are increasingly able to feed more babies

29   Tulleken, C. van, Wright, C., Brown, A., McCoy, D., & Costello, A. (2020, October 24). Marketing of Breastmilk Substitutes During the COVID-19 Pandemic. https://doi.org/10.1016/S0140-6736(20)32119-X. Retrieved August 10, 2022, from https://www.thelancet.com/journals/lancet/article/PIIS0140-6736(20)32119-X/fulltex

30   Bloomberg. (2019, October 2). Infant Formula Market Size to Reach USD 103.75 Billion by 2026. Bloomberg.com. Retrieved August 10, 2022, from https://www.bloomberg.com/press-releases/2019-10-02/infant-formula-market-size-to-reach-usd-103-75-billion-by-2026-fortune-business-insights

31   Merriam-Webster. (n.d.). Starve Definition & Meaning. Merriam-Webster. Retrieved August 10, 2022, from https://www.merriam-webster.com/dictionary/starve

by caloric standards. Food insecurity is a bitter reality for too many families. But thankfully, the mothers in the formula crisis eventually found food for their babies.

Starving Babies is a dramatic title. But the willingness of a new parent, of a supportive grandparent to pick this book up and the degree of openness they bring to this discussion may change the course of their prenatal, pregnancy, and postpartum journey. It may even shift their philosophy of parenting and their approach family health. This is not just for expecting mothers. This book is for everyone interested in the health of the next generation. Its purpose is not to scare or intimidate. Those are too often the tactics of our current system. This book offers a balance to that fear. Fear loses its power with increased understanding. Few things are scarier than the thought of birthing and feeding another human being, and the doubts that so often accompany the confidence in our ability to do so. With the right understanding and mindset, the fear and stress lose their edge. Being open and curious empowers each person navigating new parenthood themselves or supporting someone who is.

The system is failing babies when it does not provide researched, evidence-based nutrition for their growth. This is starvation in the most archaic and traditional sense. It is urgent that society, families, and parents adjust their approach. Babies need more than just calories. They need connection. That bond between mothers and infants is something we have lost along the way. No other natural link is as powerful, as important for growth and development as that.

What did humans do as a species before the powdered infant formula giant came along?

TWO:
THE HISTORY OF FEEDING BABIES: HOW DID WE GET HERE?

IN THE BEGINNING

A century of planning has shaped the current system of how modern families birth and feed their newborns. This domino line of historical events has enabled the current medical and pharmaceutical forces to win their current influence in the formula industry. The companies have evolved, the leaders have come and gone, but the mission marches relentlessly onward. They've passed their ingredients on, their plans, their relationships with government officials and agencies. No single entity is to blame for the current situation, but the target has always been and remains the same. These companies want the government to protect and pay them to become the sole source of nutrition for newborns.

Understanding what motivates this industry can help brace families against future shortages. They will see through the agendas related to these products. It can help them sort through misinformation and emotional marketing that drove so much of the growth and sales during the pandemic years. These manipulative marketing tactics would have seemed like something from an extreme hypothetical not long ago. With some awareness and accountability, perhaps it can become fiction once again.

This chapter is the origin story of the formula industry. Not surprisingly, it has a complicated relationship with the truth. Its past is checkered with ever-evolving science along with some glaring failures. Many of these were steppingstones for improvement. Some have been major stumbling blocks for the current system. Certain practices have continued into the present that, if scientists had known then what they do now, they would hopefully have demanded change. If they won't call for these changes now, though, in the face of mounting evidence, then it falls to the parents and providers to do so. Those of us with a vested interest in feeding babies must intentionally become aware and must look to the science and not the marketing. Sadly, gone are the days when the public can safely rely on the federal agencies to hold these companies accountable, as we saw in the last chapter.

Examining the history of how earlier generations have fed their children arms both new and experienced parents with perspective and information. It provides reassurance that things do get better. Humanity continues to adapt and thrive as a species, despite the fear mongering and doubt that is so often the basis of the advertising messages. Especially in times of shortages and crises, parents today can take comfort in the fact that previous generations have weathered similar storms and have found creative ways to keep children fed and growing. This is the awareness needed today to navigate the complex choices that arise when making medical and nutritional decisions for their babies.

For as long as humans have been birthing and breastfeeding babies, there have always been inherent obstacles to providing this nutrient-dense breastmilk to newborns. Mothers who were too sick or weak to breastfeed could pass their baby on to a mother who could. Entrusting another woman to breastfeed her infant is the practice of *wet nursing.* The World Health organization recommends that when a mother is unavailable or unable to produce milk, particularly in emergency situations, that the milk from another woman is preferable to artificial baby milks[32], or powdered infant formula.

Wet nursing was a common practice in 18th century Europe and early colonial America. It persists in many cultures today. It was a common belief in those times that brunettes produced better milk. (Blonde mothers should take heart that to date, this has not been verified in research.) There were strict laws for the health of women who worked in this field. Guilds of wet nurses would form, where women would share housing and support each other. They had regular examinations to ensure they were healthy enough to nurse children of those struggling with their own milk supply.

After wet nursing fell out of favor, breastmilk was substituted for that of other animals: goats, cows, mares, and donkeys. Cow milk was most readily available, but donkey milk looked more like human milk. It was often given straight from the animal or sometimes boiled and cooled for easier digestion. Some mothers diluted it with water and added sugar or honey for taste.

The baby bottle was invented during the Industrial Revolution, when it was increasingly common for mothers to be in the factories all day. Many babies drank something called pap, a concoction of boiled milk with water thickened with wheat flour and egg yolk. A similar recipe included a variety of cereals cooked in a milk broth called *panada.*

---

32   World Health Organization, United Nations Children's Fund. Guideline: updates on HIV and infant feeding: the duration of breastfeeding, and support from health services to improve feeding practices among mothers living with HIV. Geneva: World Health Organization; 2016.

In the early 1800s, a study linked consumption of cow milk with indigestion, dehydration, and higher mortality rate. It compared infants fed with cow milk and breastfed babies. One curious researcher, Johann Franz Simon published the first chemical analysis on this topic. His comparison between human and cow milk convinced him that cow milk was indigestible for infants. He attributed this to the higher protein content and bigger curd size in the cow milk.

His early studies caused doctors to recommend mixing water, sugar, and cream into cow milk. This was to help make it more digestible for infants, and the fad caught on. In 1860, one entrepreneur, Justus von Leibig marketed the first commercially produced baby food. It was a powder made from wheat flour, cow milk, potassium bicarbonate, an electrolyte, and malt flour. This "Soluble Infant Food" was $1 per bottle in 1869, which was a small fortune for that time.

Around this time and during the Civil War, Gail Borden patented a process of preserving milk by lowering its water content. He heated milk to high temperatures in sealed kettles. He added copious amounts of sugar as a preservative to extend the shelf life until the milk could reach the soldiers or families. Physicians objected to this new "sweetened condensed milk," given the high sugar content. Many mothers would dilute this and serve it to their babies when cow milk was scarce. It had the advantage of being able to be stored for much longer.

In the 1870s, the food company Nestle began offering a similar product for half the price of Leibig's, at 50 cents per bottle. It contained malt, cow milk, wheat flour, and sugar. This required only water to dilute, no milk needed, which was an added convenience. This was the first American infant food that was available in the United States.

Then in 1883, John B. Myenberg evaporated 60% of the water content out of milk and sterilized it by heating it to 200 degrees. This process is known as *homogenization* and it makes the curds much smaller and therefore more digestible. He called this *evaporated milk*. Physicians preferred this over the sweetened condensed milk because it wasn't loaded with sugar.

THE START OF PASTEURIZATION

The relatively new technique of pasteurization began in 1890 and was deployed in the dairy space. *Pasteurization* involves heating milk to a temperature that eliminates some of the harmful bacteria, resulting in a partial sterilization of the milk without changing its chemical properties too much. This process prevented milk from souring during delivery. Researchers noticed that pasteurization was lowering cases of tuberculosis, typhoid fever, cholera, and diphtheria. While scientists analyzed these exciting results, physicians strongly opposed pasteurization. Their concern was that pasteurizing milk lowered its nutritional value. They worried about killing off some healthy bacterial cultures. They were also noticing a huge increase in incidences of scurvy and rickets, two diseases caused by Vitamin C and D deficiencies.

By the turn of the century, Sears Catalog had eight different brands of infant formula. These were Horlick's Infant Food, Mellin's Infant Food, both for 75 cents per bottle, and Ridge's Food for Infants, 65 cents per bottle. In those days, these prices were simply too high for most families, and most mothers continued to breastfeed to save money. The ones that couldn't breastfeed or find a donor gave their babies cow's milk, sometimes with the cream, water, and honey or sugar mixture to help digestion.

The next big trend involved altering the carbohydrate content of the cow milk by mixing it with maltose and dextrin. In 1912, the American Medical Association, the AMA, introduced a new product to their doctors. They granted them exclusive rights to sell *Dextri-*

Maltose. They teamed up with Mead Johnson company and marketed the product through their doctors' offices.

Pasteurization became a universal practice in 1915. Many more children were being diagnosed with Vitamin C and D deficiency. This was causing rickets, which affects the healthy development of bones, as well as scurvy, with bleeding gums, and other problems affecting the immune system and mental development of babies. Physicians recommended supplementing with daily doses of orange juice and cod liver oil to combat these issues. This suggestion seemed to overcome the effects of the pasteurization.

One physician at the time wrote, "Within the past few years an increasing number of patients affected with scurvy have been brought to the Oregon Children's Hospital. As the prophylactic amount of vitamin C... is contained in 300 cc. of breast milk, scurvy is rarely found in breast-fed babies."[33]

In 1919, manufacturers attempted to solve the rising rates of scurvy and rickets. Doctors were concerned that pasteurization was lowering the vitamin content in raw milk, milk which had not been heated. Infants were not immediately sick, but a steady diet of pasteurized cow milk was resulting in vitamin deficiencies. Mothers were already supplementing the lost vitamins by adding cod liver oil and some form of Vitamin C, usually orange juice, lime or lemon juice, or potato water. Powdered infant food companies also began to replace the milk fat with fats and oils derived from animals or vegetables. They called the new product SMA, for Simulated Milk Adapted. Nestlé wanted to compete with this trend in the 1920s, so they invented Lactogen, which used only vegetable-oil as the fat source.

Doctors noticed the tremendous potential of this new, growing industry and their place in it. Mothers trusted their pediatrician's

---

33   Overstreet, R. M. (1938). The Increase of Scurvy. *Northwest Medicine.*

input; new companies were making money and were coming to them for endorsements. It seemed a win for everyone. Doctors realized the infant food companies needed their approval to really sell it to the mothers. They began to look for ways they could influence the nutritional content of this product as well. In the late 1800s, a researcher at Harvard, named Morgan Rotch, had begun developing what was known as "the percentage method." It became very popular among physicians during the first part of the 20th century.

INFANT FORMULA – THE ORIGIN STORY

Rotch thought that since cow milk contains higher casein than human milk. *Casein* is a white protein found in milk. It occurs in various ratios in different types of milk, and Rotch's studies led him to believe it ought to be diluted in cow's milk. His aim was to lower the casein ratio to match more of the profile of breastmilk. But diluting it decreased the sugar and fat content by almost half of what breastmilk contains. So Rotch added cream and sugar back into the formula in precise quantities. He taught physicians how to do the same. Doctors were trained to analyze stool from babies' diapers after a feeding. This allowed them to adjust the formula dilution accordingly. This is where the term *formula* first came into use referring to infant food, as it was generally expected that the food was *formulated* to the baby's specific needs. It was not a mass-produced product as it is known today.

In 1924, Alfred Bosworth of Harvard, a renowned milk chemist, teamed up with Henry Bowditch, a pediatrician at Boston Floating Hospital. The pair developed a competing humanized formula. They based their formula on cow's milk with varying amounts of vegetable oils. They added calcium and phosphorus salts and began experimenting with the lactose concentration, the milk sugar present in breastmilk. They ran clinical trials on 200 different formulas before settling on the right amount of lactose in their final product. They then approached the Moores and Ross Milk Company of Columbus, Ohio and even found a local brewery, the Franklin Brewery Plant, to produce it.

In 1926, the editor of the *Journal of the American Medical Association* (JAMA), Dr. Morris Fishbein, named this new formula *Similar to Lactation*, or Similac, for short. Thus, one of the major cornerstones of the formula industry was born. JAMA and the American Medical Association were the proud parents, and the Franklin Brewery Plant was the beaming midwife.

Originally, these products were intended to be sold only by physicians to mothers of their patients. The manufacturers would produce a generic, unlabeled can that could later be labeled and branded for a specific doctor. The formula was treated much like a prescription. It was only dispensed when medically necessary, and under the supervision of a physician. This was the beginning of the true medicalization of infant formula.

Not to be outdone, and still benefiting from the AMA's endorsement and exclusive distribution of Dextri-Maltose, Mead Johnson responded. They wanted to develop a soy-based formula for doctors. It was a precooked, fortified infant cereal, comprised of a mixture of wheat, oats, corn, bone meal, wheat germ, alfalfa, dried brewer's yeast, and some minerals and vitamins. They called it Sobee.

While the researchers and manufacturers played this game of one-upmanship, the American Medical Association sat back and enjoyed the show. They already saw the rewards of innovation and distribution through their pediatrician's offices. Due to the high cost of formula in the 1920s and 1930s, and perhaps the added difficulty of finding pediatricians to prescribe infant formula, many mothers still preferred to use Myenberg's *evaporated milk* instead of cow's milk, due to its smaller curd size. It was affordable, easily absorbed, and had a good shelf life. Physicians approved of the lower sugar content, and they appreciated not having to constantly check diapers and run back to their lab to mix up formula again. It wasn't as nutrient deficient as the pasteurized and diluted cow's milk.

Physicians had begun teaching mothers to mix an infant-friendly formula as early as the 1930s. They recommended 2 ounces per pound of baby's body weight per day, with 1/8 oz. of sugar and 3 oz of fluid volume per pound of body weight. By 1960, some 80% of mothers still preferred this method for its price, availability, and the ease of mixing and feeding.

The global conflicts of the First and Second World Wars boosted formula feeding rates considerably. Many mothers worked on production lines and in factories to boost domestic output for the war effort. Most had to rely on bottle feeds to sustain their babies. Commercial formulas still wouldn't become a major competitor pricewise until the 1950s. Even then, most mothers continued with what they knew from their own childhoods. These changes often take generations to solidify.

THE FOUNDATIONAL FORMULAS IN THE 1950s

The 1950s saw several important developments in commercial formula production. In 1951, Ross Laboratories figured out how to concentrate Similac. Mead Johnson produced the famous Enfamil, short for *infant milk*. By 1956, the rate of American exclusive breastfeeding at six months had fallen to 20%, the lowest recorded up to that time. Some doctors were taught in medical school to openly discourage breastfeeding. The cultural expectation was undergoing a radical shift. The mothers of this era frequently faced hostility and opposition if they decided to breastfeed their babies. Often their mothers and grandmothers held traditional views on the importance of breastfeeding, and they would continue to encourage and support them.

1959 saw the launch of Similac fortified with iron. But the product was not well received because many mothers believed the iron caused diarrhea or constipation in their babies. In 1967, the American Academy of Pediatrics established a Committee on Nutrition to make the first recommendations for the nutritional content of infant formula. They intended to revise their nutritional standards periodically as new data and discoveries were available. After distributing their nutritional findings, iron deficiency anemia in newborns dropped strikingly. The iron content in breastmilk, they learned, is important to the formation of healthy blood cells in babies.

By the 1970s, the tide had finally turned in favor of commercial formulas. Evaporated milk finally lost its status as the standard for nutrition. This is likely due to the ease of use, the availability, and low cost of alternative methods of feeding. Much of the messaging from this era focused on *medically approved* formulas. They leveraged the full force of medical authority to convince mothers formula was optimal nutrition for infants. One of the biggest driving forces for the growth of the infant formula market also began in this decade. It was a marketing tactic so clever it would plant powdered infant formula forever in the mainstream mind.

Formula makers also began deploying *mothercraft nurses*, who were dressed in uniforms that looked identical to the white ones worn by the nurses in the hospital. They would visit hospital maternity wards or go door-to-door to homes of newly delivered mothers. Sometimes they would simply wait outside hospitals for parents to come out pushing a stroller with their new baby. These saleswomen would recommend formula feeding and promote their company's brand of formula. Using the nurse uniforms drew some intense criticism, and the formula companies eventually eliminated the uniforms, then scrapped the mothercraft sales approach altogether. But they found a better way to promote their product: using actual healthcare providers.

A BOLD, NEW TACTIC

It is known today as *medical detailing*.[34] Formula manufacturers wanted the endorsement of hospitals and pediatricians to push their product. They realized the easiest way to get a new mom hooked on their product was to provide free samples upon hospital delivery of the baby. These gift baskets would build brand loyalty. When mom believed she could only feed her baby this certain brand, it made her less sensitive to changes in prices. This meant manufacturers could increase their prices without losing customers, all because they were hooked on their first dose. One of Abbott Laboratories' sales training manuals from 1975 states "When one considers that for every 100 infants discharged on a particular formula brand, approximately 93 infants remain on that brand, the importance of hospital selling becomes obvious." An Abbott Laboratories trade publication also stated, "In effect, we are striving to make the physician a low-pressure salesman for Abbott."[35]

Formula manufacturers would first win over hospital administration, then the doctors and nurses, and anyone who had patient contact where they could influence a decision for formula feeding. In 1974, Abbott signed a contract with New York City, guaranteeing "that every new mother leaving a municipal hospital would be given a free one-day supply of Similac."[36]

---

34 Economic Research Service, Oliveira, V., Prell, M., Smallwood, D., & Frazao, E., WIC and the Retail Price of Infant Formula (2004). United States Department of Agriculture. Retrieved August 21, 2022, from https://www.ers.usda.gov/webdocs/publications/46787/15976_fanrr39-1_1_.pdf?v=0.

35 Baer, E. (1982, April). *Babies Means Business*. New Internationalist. Retrieved September 19, 2022, from https://newint.org//features/1982/04/01/babies/

36 The New York Times. (1981, October 27). *Study on infant formula use.* The New York Times. Retrieved September 19, 2022, from https://www.nytimes.com/1981/10/27/style/study-on-infant-formula-use.html

This practice was widespread, and many practitioners recall fondly the cruises, ski vacations, and lavish gifts they would receive from formula manufacturers, trying to secure loyalty among hospital staff. Just as in the early days, the formula manufacturers relied on the medical authorities to put the expert endorsement behind their products. They began to do this in increasing amounts, and the American Academy of Pediatrics began by accepting a renewable grant for $1 million from Abbott Laboratories. Around the same time, Nestlé approached the Indian Academy of Pediatrics with a similar cash offer. They, however, were rejected to avoid the inevitable and glaring conflict of interest that such a gift would create for India.

Manufacturers began with powdered formula, which required special rooms to clean and mix bottles. Then they started concentrating liquid formulas and during this decade, donated them to hospitals, free of charge. Hospitals provided these ready-to-feed bottles to babies. They phased out formula preparation rooms. Mothers noticed the convenience and prevalence of the ready-to-feed packaging and decided to continue it at home. 1971 saw the lowest-ever breastfeeding attempts of only 25% of mothers trying to breastfeed in the hospital. Successful breastfeeding at six months of age was less than 6%. Many pediatricians and obstetricians, while not directly disparaging breastfeeding, certainly weren't encouraging the practice. The convenience of ready-to-feed products trumped almost all other considerations.

FORMULA ENTERS INTERNATIONAL MARKETS

Also, during this decade, a slight decline in the Western birth rate stalled the formula industry expansion. Nestlé particularly, but other manufacturers as well, faced considerable opposition as they entered foreign markets, attempting to pad their slowing profits.[37] The motives of this company specifically were called into question when they launched *just add water* formulas. These were being sold to populations in the developing world without access to safe drinking water. Without the mother's own immune system to protect the breastmilk supply, infants were consuming formula that was contaminated as soon as it was mixed with the local water. One nurse, Fatima Patel, worked closely with Peruvian mothers. She testified before the United States subcommittee in the 1978 hearings.

"The river is used as a laundry, as a bathroom, as a toilet and for drinking water... to get the fuel to boil that water, she has to go into the jungle, chop a tree trunk with a machete... and carry it on her back. No mother is going to use that hard-earned piece of wood to boil that water. So, the babies are drinking the contaminated water," Patel said.[38] There was also difficulty in properly cleaning bottles for the feeding. Most households only had access to only one pot, and to use it to sterilize baby bottles was just not feasible. Many times, if babies did not finish the bottle, mothers would store it. In equatorial climates, without refrigeration, this bottle would quickly become an incubator for deadly bacteria. This was another common source of fatal infant infections.

Some mothers in emerging markets were mixing the formula incorrectly, which was diluting it too much for baby's health. They would add as much as three times the recommended amount of water, severely impacting the nutrition of the formula.[39] It was also shutting down mothers' own milk supply while the baby was formula fed. Due to the unreliable nature of the supply chain in these evolving

37   Solomon, S. (1981, December 6). *The Controversy Over Infant Formula*. Retrieved September 19, 2022, from https://www.nytimes.com/1981/12/06/magazine/the-controversy-over-infant-formula.html?pagewanted=all

38

39   Muller, M. (1974). *The Baby Killer*. London; War on Want.

economies, distribution of formula was spotty. Shortages were common. Many mothers were unable to afford the ongoing cost of the formula. Bottle-feeding at that time cost about a dollar a day in the United States, but that was one half of the average daily wage in some of these countries. Without a natural supply to fall back on, a steady supply they can afford to purchase, or any alternatives like wet nurses, babies paid the ultimate price.

However, once rural populations in developing countries realized that their children were missing out on immune system protection from breastmilk, many chose to cut out the formula entirely and resume breastfeeding practices. In one pivotal study, now known as the Puriscal Study conducted in Costa Rica, this return to breastfeeding lowered infant diarrhea by 91%, meningitis cases dropped by 92%, and lower respiratory infection fell 43%. Overall infant mortality rates from infections dropped 81%, simply by ending formula feeding and returning babies to breastfeeding.[40]

Seeing similar results in these developing economies, the United Nations subcommittee on nutrition listed powdered infant formula and bottle feeding far down on their list of recommendations. If a mother is unable to breastfeed, they recommended she find a wet nurse among her family. If this was not possible, animal milk or other processed milk alternatives, like evaporated or powdered skim milk would do. They were even urged to consider yogurt in places without reliable refrigeration. They also recommended using a cup and a spoon to feed the baby, instead of a bottle with a nipple, since these are easier to clean and sanitize between feeds.

---

40   Mata Jiménez, L., Sáenz, P., Araya, J. R., Allen, M. de los Á., García, M. E., & Carvajal, J. J. (1988, September 1). *Promotion of Breastfeeding in Costa Rica: the Puriscal study*. Repositorio Institucional de la Universidad de Costa Rica. Retrieved September 19, 2022, from https://www.kerwa.ucr.ac.cr/handle/10669/15562

All this is a cautionary tale for mothers who are facing the reality of the current formula shortages. Many mothers today are used to online ordering with same-day delivery from retailers, or routinely walk into grocery stores with a staggering variety of products. When certain products disappear off the shelves due to breakdowns in a complex system that keeps them there, the panic sets in. Observing the formula crises in these developing nations from the 1970s should cause parents to think about the stability of their own access to reliable infant nutrition. If mother's milk supply ended, and they were unable to secure formula, what would the backup plan be?

1978 and '79 were crucial years for establishing formula standards. The country witnessed the rise of a condition called *hypochloremic metabolic alkalosis*, and infants were diagnosed with an electrolyte imbalance. The response to this problem was so monumental in the formula industry that the next chapter is entirely focused on this time period and episode. It set enormous precedent for the industry at large.

By 1997, Ross began reformulating Similac's whey and casein ratios, the two key proteins in breastmilk and infant formula. They continued to fine tune the humanization of these products. This attempt led one researcher to observe, "For us to think that in 40 years we can duplicate what has happened in four million years of human development is very arrogant."[41]

MODERN SOLUTIONS

In 2003, Mead Johnson followed suit by making small adjustments to the Enfamil ratios. Both formula makers added nucleotides, attempting to match the levels found in human milk. They both began to introduce

---

41   Solomon, S. (1981, December 6). *The Controversy Over Infant Formula*. Retrieved September 19, 2022, from https://www.nytimes.com/1981/12/06/magazine/the-controversy-over-infant-formula. html?pagewanted=all

formulas that contained more long-chain polyunsaturated fatty acids. These were key elements in getting even closer to real human milk.

Also in the late 1990s, the European Union and the World Health Organization began adding docosahexaenoic acid (DHA) and arachidonic acid (AA) to formula. Research was increasingly pointing to the importance of these two ingredients in boosting brain development. Children who consumed breastmilk or who were given formula that included DHA and AA showed higher IQ scores. This concept will be discussed in a future chapter in more detail. These are naturally occurring, safe constituents in natural breastmilk.

The EU and WHO researchers recommended the American formula-makers follow suit. There had never been a serious question on their safety, since they are naturally present in breastmilk. Research showed overwhelming evidence for promoting development of the central nervous system. The European Union is constantly updating infant formula and nutritional recommendations, based on their research. The American Food and Drug Administration has made one official update since 1985. This may be a partial reason why it took until 2015 for American manufacturers to include these ingredients in formula.[42] And even then, they only added half the recommended dosage of European research.

HOW CLEAN ARE FORMULA INGREDIENTS?

In 2011, the Environmental Protection Agency tested 300 samples of soybeans. 271 of the samples showed residue of the popular weedkiller Round-Up®.[43] Round-Up® contains a chemical called glyphosate. This

42   Szalinski, C. (19AD). *A very expensive, technically illegal workaround to the formula shortage*. The Atlantic. Retrieved August 18, 2022, from https://www.msn.com/en-us/news/us/rich-parents-are-tapping-into-a-baby-formula-black-market/ar-AAXtJed
43   Gillam, C. (2015, April 17). *U.S. regulators may recommend testing food for glyphosate residues*. Reuters. Retrieved August 10, 2022, from https://www.reuters.com/article/us-food-agriculture-glyphosate/u-s-regulators-may-recommend-testing-food-for-glyphosate-residues-idUSKBN0N82K020150417

a major product of the company Monsanto and has been in popular use since the 1970s. Glyphosate is controversial, since recent studies have found that it is present in food, like these soybeans tested, but also in soil, air, water, including rain. The World Health Organization's *International Agency for Research on Cancer* recently concluded that glyphosate is "probably carcinogenic to humans,"[44] meaning it could cause cancer. At any rate, exposure to this chemical has increased at least five-fold[45] in the last two decades.

Ten countries have either banned glyphosate use altogether or are in the process of doing so. An additional fifteen have restricted its use. Certain US cities and states have banned its use as well. After the soybean study, Monsanto carefully positioned themselves in the public perception as a concerned, responsible company. They were acquired in 2016 by the multinational pharmaceutical company Bayer and announced plans to begin removing glyphosate from lawn and garden products, since this is where most of their consumer lawsuits originate. This process would be concluded by 2023. Bayer stated said this was to "mitigate litigation risk"[46] to the company, and not over any safety concerns. After the chemical was named as a potential cancer-causing agent, it opened the floodgates for lawsuits.

However, internal emails dating all the way back to 2002 contained the admission "Glyphosate is OK but the formulated product (and thus the surfactant) does the damage."[47] They go on to say "We had a close call vis-à-vis mutagenicity/EU review a couple years ago." The email then discusses ways to be informed of similar studies in advance so

---

44   Guyton KZ, Loomis D, Grosse Y, El Ghissassi F, Benbrahim-Tallaa L, Guha N, Scoccianti C, Mattock H, Straif K, International Agency for Research on Cancer Monograph Working Group ILF. Carcinogenicity of tetrachlorvinphos, parathion, malathion, diazinon, and glyphosate. Lancet Oncol. 2015;16:490-491.

45   Mills PJ, Kania-Korwel I, Fagan J, McEvoy LK, Laughlin GA, Barrett-Connor E. Excretion of the Herbicide Glyphosate in Older Adults Between 1993 and 2016. JAMA. 2017;318(16):1610-1611. doi:10.1001/jama.2017.11726

46   Bayer. (2022, July 28). *Bayer Provides Update on Path to Closure of Roundup™ Litigation*. Bayer Global. Retrieved September 15, 2022, from https://www.bayer.com/media/en-us/bayer-provides-update-on-path-to-closure-of-rounduptm-litigation/

47   (2002, April 25). Heydens, *RE: European commission Endocrine Disrupters developments (1)*.

they can "get response ready and distribute it proactively."[48] The same email talks about the specialists and experts in various fields they can inform about their product, to "establish a network of prestigious scientists."

This is not how science is supposed to work. A company should not be doing their own research or buying up spokespeople who they position as so-called experts. They should not have the power to squelch findings. This internal exchange shows how well these companies are playing the game, how versed in manipulating public perception and legislative action they have become. That was, incidentally, the first and last time the USDA or EPA ever checked soy for the presence of glyphosate.

This is particularly important for expecting mothers or those planning to breastfeed their babies. Glyphosate has been detected in over 90% of pregnant women and has been linked to shorter pregnancies and increased risks to babies[49]. In one study, none of the toxin was found in the water supply, meaning the exposure was coming from somewhere else. When the possibility of cancer and mutations is being discussed, many experts are calling for lawmakers to err on the side of caution until glyphosate can be safely determined. This will require studies that are backed by a neutral third party, and not the parent company.

The FDA and the EPA do not seem to actively be weighing in on these issues when a large part of the international community is voicing concerns over these chemicals. If these toxins are present in the soy that's being fed to newborns, or if mothers are being exposed to five times the amount today, it should raise questions on the cleanliness

---

48   (2002, April 25). Farmer, *RE: European commission Endocrine Disrupters developments (1)*.
49   Parvez, S., Gerona, R.R., Proctor, C. et al. Glyphosate exposure in pregnancy and shortened gestational length: a prospective Indiana birth cohort study. Environ Health 17, 23 (2018). https://doi.org/10.1186/s12940-018-0367-0

of the environment. This could be accumulating in the umbilical cord and the bloodstream of newborns. One would expect this to be a concern of the Environmental Protection Agency, due to its impact on our soil, air, water, and food supply. If food contaminated with this toxin is sourced and used for infant formula, it should be a concern of the Food and Drug Administration, but no such intervention seems to be materializing. Who, exactly, are these agencies beholden to, if not the American taxpayer and their babies?

Companies, meanwhile, continue diversifying their formula lines, many continuing to source questionable ingredients at the lowest possible cost, with no real discernible regard for the as-of-yet unknown risks. They carve out special niches for different types of consumers. Products like lactose-free, soy with dietary fiber, and rice starch-based formulas for acid reflux help them stand out on the shelf.

FORMULA SHORTAGES AND GOVERNMENT

There is one major thing that determines the rise and fall of all these product lines and of the companies who bring them to market. That is winning bids for state contracts to become the sole supplier for government programs.

Overnight, subtle shifts in policy can make or break an entire company's fortune. To understand that parents should know a little more about the current system US policymakers have established. These are the few rules that these corporations play by. It directly impacts their bottom line, and their access to their consumers.

Small, subtle shudders have carefully redirected public perceptions on an almost subconscious level for most of the history of this industry. However, once in a generation or so, a large swing in some aspect of this complicated system grabs the national attention. Such was the case with the recent Sturgis factory shutdown, the ensuing national formula shortage, and the media's coverage of how the Biden administration addressed the matter.

Former White House Press Secretary Jen Psaki's recent handling was a textbook illustration of the issue. Following the demonstrably false, alarmist statements she made regarding the Abbott outbreak on her final day in office[50], one journalist posed the question: "...If you can't find formula and you need it for your baby to eat, what should [parents] be doing?"

Psaki responded, "We would certainly encourage any parent who has concerns about their child's health or wellbeing to call their doctor or a pediatrician."[51] While sidestepping the issue of which agency is ultimately handling the matter, she also demonstrated the subtle slide towards the medical takeover of formula feeding, at least in the minds of the White House's mind. This was no longer a question for the food suppliers or retailers of the country. It certainly didn't seem to be a concern for the White House. It was something that she viewed as falling under the medical umbrella. Other suggestions included checking with a pediatrician's office to see if they had free samples on hand or could write a prescription for direct shipping of formula to the home. Each of these alternatives is slowly and steadily nudging the masses back towards their medical providers and local pharmacies for feeding their babies.

Psaki's successor in the position, Karine Jean-Pierre, after the formula shortages persisted far beyond the anticipated reopening of Sturgis, was asked what actions the administration was taking. "Ensuring that infant formula is safe and available for families across the country is a top priority for the White House and this administration.

---

50   Goodin, E. (2022, May 12). *'Babies Died': Jen Psaki Defends the Government's Closure of Abbott Plant.* Daily Mail Online. Retrieved August 31, 2022, from https://www.dailymail.co.uk/news/article-10811079/Babies-died-Jen-Psaki-DEFENDS-governments-closure-Abbott-plant.html

51   *Asked what parents should do if they can't find formula, Jen Psaki says call a doctor.* Grabien. (n.d.). Retrieved August 31, 2022, from https://grabien.com/story.php?id=378199

We know that Abbott's voluntary recall of infant formula products has led to some Americans being unable to access other critical medical food supply. This is an urgent issue that the FDA and White House are working 24/7 to address," the replacement White House Press Secretary stated.

One reporter followed up with the logical question "Who is running point on the formula issue at the White House? You mentioned the White House is involved."

"At the White House, I don't know," laughs the White House Press Secretary Jean-Pierre.[52] For parents with laser-like focus on where their baby's next meal is coming from, such a flippant and calloused attitude was taken by many parents as a slap in the face. Those observing this drama as it unfolds are beginning to realize that nobody is coming to save them from bad companies in such powerful and profitable positions.

Why is all this relevant? Because it's about to change dramatically and permanently. This is somewhat akin to living on the cusp of the evaporated milk discovery, during the movement to humanize formula, or other major discoveries during the last century of formula production. One such development is planned very soon that could change the powdered infant formula world significantly.

MILK-LIKE PRODUCT FROM BIOREACTORS

During the 2020 panic and pablum of the COVID-19 worldwide noise, a quiet move occurred that hardly garnered any media attention. A company called Biomilq formed, run by a woman named Leila Strickland. It's based on a new concept, as revolutionary as Carnation's

---

52   Pavlich, K. (2022, May 11). *Biden's incoming press secretary laughs when asked who is handling baby formula crisis.* Townhall. Retrieved August 31, 2022, from https://townhall.com/tipsheet/katiepavlich/2022/05/11/bidens-incoming-press-secretary-laughs-about-baby-formula-shortage-n2607079

Evaporated Milk. It has as much profit potential as any powdered infant formula ever did. It's called *mammary biotechnology*. This is a new form of biotechnology based on the idea of growing human milk in a lab. This biotech company quietly began culturing *mammary epithelial cells*, or *MECs*, which are the specialized cells that produce breastmilk in breast tissue.

Biomilq is hoping to be one of the first companies to mass-produce *human-like* product. Historically, that was what milk chemists and infant formula manufacturers obsessed over. Now the science is putting the production of laboratory-made human milk within reach. Once the process has been approved and released, this product could take the industry by storm. No longer will there be worry over protein ratios, carbohydrates, and liquid amounts. Babies will now have the option of a synthetic version of human milk on demand.

This technology has the potential to dominate the formula space unless parents and pediatricians understand the science and accept the tradeoffs. They need to be made aware of what those are, because it is unlikely the advertisers will feel the need to do so. Their job is to sell the product, not necessarily to educate on the drawbacks. Within this generation, it could be the new fad. Which is why parents need to be prepared with the facts and the agenda at work here. The men and the money behind may come as little surprise.

The CEO of Biomilq, Michelle Egger, claims that the idea came to her when she first learned about lab-grown hamburger. Her origin story is as quaint as it is contrived. As a food scientist, she decided that if science could now make a burger without killing a cow, culturing specialized *meat cells* in a bioreactor, it should be able to do the same thing with human milk.

Egger is a former member of the Gates Foundation.[53] She is backed by billionaire Bill Gates, and several of his cronies: Jeff Bezos, Mark Zuckerberg, and Jack Ma to name a few. Some of these men have faced recent criticism for discussing topics like population control and the need to enforce certain medical interventions.

The science involved in the milk-like product is quite complex, but is evolving quickly, goaded on by some of these heavy-hitting investors. There are strong green energy movement incentives. The opportunity comes as the traditional powdered formula industry is sputtering and destabilizing. The more the national infant formula supply suffers, the better an alternative like Biomilq looks as a possible solution to the current situation.

A mother can donate her own breastmilk to the company, which contains living tissue, the mammary epithelial cells. These are screened out and selected to ensure they are the correct milk-producing cells needed. They are cultured in an environment carefully controlled to resemble the conditions of a human breast.[54]

Once these cells have spread out along the lining to which they are attached, their environment is flooded with the building blocks of human milk. They are then exposed to prolactin, the hormone that signals milk production. The entire mixture is allowed to incubate while the cells do their job at turning out *milk-like product.*

The public is already being assured that this method is cheaper than formula to produce and more carbon-friendly for the earth (although nobody has calculated the exact numbers yet). The company's website is worded carefully, even strategically. They pay their dutiful lip service to the *breast is best* crowd. They claim their

53   Roy, A. (2020, June 16). *Bill Gates' climate-change investment firm bets on lab-produced breast milk.* CNBC. Retrieved August 10, 2022, from https://www.cnbc.com/2020/06/16/biomilq-raises-3point5-million-from-bill-gates-investment-firm.html

54   *Our science.* BIOMILQ. (n.d.). Retrieved August 10, 2022, from https://www.biomilq.com/our-science

product "will contain much of the nutrition of breastmilk with the practicality of formula."[55]

Comparing the human-like product to the safety and efficacy of formula requires more information and history than is currently available. Recently, the company closed a $21 million investment in Schedule A early term investments.[56] Their mission statements have very flowery language, focusing on health and nature. However, their investor strategy places primary emphasis on the fact they are women-run. They tout an investor board that's diverse.

What they don't mention is important. Since it is so new, there exists no medical or manufacturing governing board that can evaluate their health claims, no standard way of monitoring the production and distribution process. They screen their breastmilk donors and incentivize them with Target gift cards[57]. This practice causes some serious doubt on the motivation and manipulation threshold of the entire system, top to bottom. The ethics of voluntary, not-for-compensation donation of tissues like blood and even breastmilk, is quickly called into question under this current model. Most prevailing research and the general sentiment overall regarding blood donation is that "offering money or cash-equivalent incentives... may have a negative effect on blood safety and blood donor contribution."[58] Similar thoughts prevail with regards to donor milk safety.

Donors who give breastmilk without financial compensation have no motivation to tamper with the milk or their own personal health information. They are assumed to donate out of purely altruistic

---

55 *About Us.* BIOMILQ. (n.d.). Retrieved September 15, 2022, from https://www.biomilq.com/about

56 Sousa, R. (2021, October 21). *Biomilq secures $21M in series A funding round.* FoodBev Media. Retrieved August 10, 2022, from https://www.foodbev.com/news/biomilq-secures-21m-in-series-a-funding-round/

57 Chan, M. (2022, May 3). *This startup is creating 'human milk' in a lab.* CNN. Retrieved August 10, 2022, from https://edition.cnn.com/2022/05/03/business/lab-grown-human-milk-biomilq-health-climate-hnk-spc-intl/index.html

58 Abolghasemi, H., Hosseini-Divkalayi, N. S., & Seighali, F. (2010). Blood donor incentives: A step forward or backward. Asian journal of transfusion science, 4(1), 9–13. https://doi.org/10.4103/0973-6247.59385

motivations without any potential conflict of interest. Biomilq's incentivization of donors with gift cards could be construed as a moral gray area. In extreme cases, profit motive could put children at risk if caregivers feel pressured to sell the milk that would otherwise feed them. There is also the concern of adulterated supply to increase its volume.[59] One study found that approximately 10% of online breastmilk purchases have been found to have been mixed with cow milk[60]. This would likely not be an issue with Biomilq's model since the product is heavily screened after it is received, instead of just consumed.

Biomilq is the only company in the US currently engaged in this sort of development. There is one other company in Singapore racing to bring their product to market.[61] This will likely supply much of the Asian demand for formula alternatives.

When a baby latches at the breast, there is a complex system that engages. This provides the nutrition of the breastmilk, but it also comes with a host of other immune system benefits as we will read in future chapters. Considering the complexity of this exchange between the baby's latch and mother's immune system, breastmilk can't be simply mass-produced, stored, and sold. There are so many complex ingredients and cellular activities in breastmilk researchers have yet to account for. They are still working to catalog the recommended daily or even hourly intake of all these crucial components for optimal infant health. That entire dance is innately coordinated between mother and infant.

59   Grey, H. (2018, January 4). *Breast Milk Banks: Should women be paid?* Healthline. Retrieved September 8, 2022, from https://www.healthline.com/health-news/compensation-for-donating-breast-milk

60   Sarah A. Keim, Manjusha M. Kulkarni, Kelly McNamara, Sheela R. Geraghty, Rachael M. Billock, Rachel Ronau, Joseph S. Hogan, Jesse J. Kwiek; Cow's Milk Contamination of Human Milk Purchased via the Internet. Pediatrics May 2015; 135 (5): e1157–e1162. 10.1542/peds.2014-3554

61   Selby, G. (2021, April 27). *Future of milk: Singapore start-up TurtleTree expands to us to leverage food tech growth.* Food Ingredients First. Retrieved August 10, 2022, from https://www.foodingredientsfirst.com/news/future-of-milk-singapore-start-up-turtletree-expands-to-us-to-leverage-food-tech-growth.html

This milk-like product has demonstrated no prolonged benefit on the developing infant's immunology because that exchange between living, intelligent systems would be totally absent in lab-produced product. It certainly would hold no benefit hormonally or neurologically for either infant or mother. It's empty food. It has calories but lacks connection. It is disconnecting the infant from nature. The infant bond is an essential part of raising a stable, well-connected child. There is far more neurology than nutrition that occurs during the breastfeeding process. There is also considerable immune system support from breastfeeding. This product wouldn't address that either.

Biomilq has pointed to several of the problems of alternative solutions to the existing system. They point out that donor breast milk is costly to screen and store, and distribution and consumption can cost over $100 a day.[62] The theory with mammary biotechnology is that milk-producing cells in a bioreactor can generate more product than human breast tissue can. They believe they can do it at a lower cost and as they consistently point out, with less carbon footprint and greater diversity of their board of investors.

This concept has the potential to become the next alternative to powdered infant formula. It has the advantage of being a new, exciting technology, along with a carefully crafted narrative about being comparable to breastmilk. In such a tightly controlled market, it exists separate from international research review. It is immune to multinational legislation on best practices in marketing, because no such standard exists in the United States, even for the powdered formula industry. Given the current crises and shortages, this company could seize advantages over existing competitors as they define the newly emerging biotechnology in their ideal image. So far, their challenge is

_____

62   Chan, M. (2022, May 3). *This startup is creating 'human milk' in a lab.* CNN. Retrieved August 10, 2022, from https://edition.cnn.com/2022/05/03/business/lab-grown-human-milk-biomilq-health-climate-hnk-spc-intl/index.html

unanswered in its attempt to do so. The men and the money behind this enterprise have shown their willingness to purchase entire sectors of the economy. They've managed to outmaneuver the FDA on drug approvals. They've successfully subjugated representatives in government to their ambitions.

If left unchecked either by government oversight or consumer awareness, Biomilq could take the system by storm. Their rise comes with some very serious potential pitfalls. As their technology is created and patented, they begin to pick their way through the bureaucracy of the USDA and FDA. These standards are unprecedented for such a huge and groundbreaking product. Nobody knows better than Bill Gates that when a shortage or a so-called emergency is declared, red tape can be slashed at record speed. Conventional safety tests, clinical trials, and consumer recourse are among the first to fall by the wayside. They become the sacrifice to the urgency of the situation. His same methods apply for his company Biomilq as they do for anything else he's brought to market. When almost half of the US formula disappears, many parents gladly accept ready-to-feed "milk-like products." Like most of their food, they don't mind that it comes from a lab. These are as close to breastmilk as the Impossible Burger ever was to home-grown Angus beef.

A sincere discussion on how babies are fed should also involve the immunology and the neurology of that bond between mother and child. It doesn't focus just on the availability of human milk and the convenience and economy of its production and delivery. It acknowledges the natural necessity of breastmilk, looking at the *entire picture* of infant nutrition. By natural design, it takes a village to feed and support a new mother and her baby. Before the village, though, it takes a family.

Natural law requires a provider that can support and sustain the mother not only through those difficult nine months but beyond, during breastfeeding. There will always be a *dyad*, a matched set, a provider and a nurturer. And when no such provider is to be found, the government and the formula or human-milk producers eagerly step in to become either the provider to the mother, or to become the mother to that child. The mother can then return to her new, socially assigned role as the provider. This entire system is experimental in the human story, and its outcomes must be examined. Is this model winning the battle for maternal and infant health?

The government and Big Bottle industries have so subtly and seamlessly stepped into this role. They've capitalized on crises, on shortages, on disease outbreaks to consolidate their control of infant feeding. They've worked to replace mothers as early in the process as they can. And while babies are being fed calories and nutrients, they are starving for connection.

THREE:
THE POLITICS OF THE FORMULA INDUSTRY

HOW "THE ACT" CAME TO BE

One warm, muggy summer afternoon in Memphis, Tennessee, on Thursday, July 26, 1979, a pediatrician picked up a phone and made a report to the Centers for Disease Control and Prevention, the CDC. He was concerned about three cases of infants, all younger than 10 months of age who were failing to gain weight. The babies had poor appetites, and one had a history of constipation. Blood work showed low chloride and calcium levels. They had varying degrees of alkalinity in their blood pH. They also had microscopic traces of blood in their urine. He noticed that all three consumed the same soy-based formula, called Neo-Mull-Soy, manufactured by Syntex.

The CDC moved with lightning speed. By the very next day, a Friday, the CDC's *Epidemic Intelligence Service*, or *EIS*, began their first day of work on the CDC's Birth Defects Branch. They had a plan to send out a survey to all pediatric nephrologists to identify other infants with similar symptoms. The EIS surveyed pediatric nephrologists throughout the country for similar cases. They were looking for infants diagnosed with failure to thrive, *anorexia*, the technical term for a lack of appetite, or constipation. The infants in the study ranged from two to nine months old. They came from different locations and both genders.

The nationwide survey only turned up fifteen additional cases. The CDC realized they needed more data points. They identified sixteen more cases, virtually overnight, from "other sources" that gave them the convenient statistical threshold of 31 cases.

Twenty-seven of the babies had a feeding history. Twenty-six of those were consuming the same formula as the initial three. It was Neo-Mull-Soy, which comprised about 10% of the soy-based formula market at that time. After diagnosing high pH levels in the bloodstream, something called *alkalosis*, they supplemented the infants with chloride, essentially salt. All of them responded favorably. Once their pH levels normalized, they returned to the soy formula. They then had a recurrence of the alkalosis.

This *chloride-responsive alkalosis* has another name. It's a salt deficiency. These dehydrated babies need more salt to retain water in their bodies and to help normalize the chemical balance in their tissues. The chloride supplementation was simply increasing the babies' salt and fluid intake. The ions from the salt made their bodies more acidic, and things returned to normal.

Syntex recalled Neo-Mull-Soy and halted all production. They informed pediatricians and pediatric residents of the issue. Infants that switched to other soy-based formulas besides Neo-Mull-Soy did not have the same issue. The daily value of salt for babies at that time was unknown. Neo-Mull-Soy, they inferred, must have contained insufficient amounts of chloride. The CDC initiated a follow-up investigation in 1979. They started a registry of children with similar symptoms consuming this formula. and one other it identified as chloride-deficient was Cho-Free, another soy brand also manufactured by Syntex.

The original diagnosis for the three Tennessee infants was something called Bartter Syndrome. This was a newly named and rare genetic condition that would not have responded to supplementation. Since the babies improved, the first diagnosis was discarded. By expanding their focus beyond the original diagnosis, the CDC pointed to chloride deficiency as the culprit. They found it in two soy-based formulas that affected the 31 infants.

Fortunately, none of the infants died. A later study by the *National Institutes of Health* focused on the effects of chloride deficiency. They determined that by age 10, most children had recovered from early delayed growth. Their report found that "exposure to the chloride-deficient formulas Neo-Mull-Soy or Cho-Free during infancy has not resulted in any long-term adverse effects on cognitive development."[63]

America could heave a sigh of relief, right? This was the medical world and the government working together to save our babies from low salt intake. Well, the most suspicious part of this entire episode is the timing of the events. Here is a brief review the timeline on record:

The Tennessee doctor misdiagnosed three infants with electrolyte imbalance as Bartter Syndrome. The day after he spoke with the CDC they staffed the EIS. The two men in that unit reported to their first day in the new position on Friday, July 27, 1979. They weren't about to let a crisis like this go to waste.

By the following Monday, July 30th, they sent a nationwide survey to pediatric nephrologists. They must have pulled weekend hours, or had the questionnaire prepared in advance. By Wednesday, August 1st, two days later, one of the new EIS officers was on a plane to Syntex headquarters with corporate leadership in Palo Alto, California. What sort of data drove such a high-profile meeting on such short notice?

63   Malloy, M. H., Graubard, B., Moss, H., McCarthy, M., Gwyn, S., Vietze, P., Willoughby, A., Rhoads, G. G., & Berendes, H. (1991). Hypochloremic metabolic alkalosis from ingestion of a chloride-deficient infant formula: outcome 9 and 10 years later. Pediatrics, 87(6), 811–822.

Has a government agency ever worked this fast? Certainly not in the case of the Sturgis shutdown with the FDA. Was this a coordinated, pre-scheduled response? Was it administrative action waiting to happen?

The CDC representative from the EIS office met with the company's top leadership. Three other pediatricians joined them who had reportedly already tested several batches of formula. They had also already determined the batches had insufficient chloride levels. The very next day, August 2nd, Syntex leadership met with FDA representatives. In available records, there is no mention of how they became involved, or at what point they showed up in California. The company ceased production that Thursday. They initiated a recall. They notified healthcare professionals of the deficiency of Neo-Mull-Soy and Cho-Free.

This was all accomplished in less than seven days from the onset of the initial observation, including the weekend. And at a time when mailgrams and telephone were the fastest, most secure forms of communication, how did this all move so fast? It may seem like nothing major, a salt deficiency affecting a purported thirty-one newborns. It was two products composing a fraction of the soy-based formula market.

However, the events of this week led to the creation of the *Infant Formula Act of 1980*. This was the first landmark piece of legislation that brought infant formula firmly under the FDA's regulatory jurisdiction. The formulation and production of powdered infant food became officially the home territory of a federal agency. This was a major step in the medicalization of the formula industry.

The content of the legislation deals less with paltry details like the salt content of baby formula, although it did address this. It is far more concerned with the regulation of companies in that space. Congress ruled that infant formula could no longer be marketed without prior FDA approval. Logically, this would make it more difficult and expensive for new companies to get formula approved. The country was already facing a serious lag in drug approval time. Now Congress had created a formula lag problem too, with the passage of the *Infant Formula Act of 1980*.

The act requires each manufacturer of an infant formula to notify the government of any change in formula processed. They are required to conduct tests to ensure it is not adulterated. If they suspect formula is a risk to human health, they must alert authorities. It directs the agency how to determine the scope and extent of any necessary recall. It also establishes reporting and recordkeeping standards. This is so that in the event of a recall, they can trace and monitor the product.

This legislation would shape the next several decades of the infant formula sector. The high barriers of entry and huge cost of bringing additional products to market would more closely resemble the pharmaceutical world than the food industry. Any major players were now safely barricaded in the industry against any new competitors. They began to negotiate for government contracts in the welfare space as many drug manufacturers did.

FORMULA CONTRACTS AND THE BUSINESS OF WELFARE

The formula welfare system enshrines the worst parts of the pharmaceutical model. It drives out competition. It increases profits for the companies in power. And it encourages them to consolidate production in a few critical sites to keep their costs down. These have already proven to be prone to contamination, shut down, and shortage. Despite centralizing production, which should make oversight and compliance easier, the crisis with Sturgis points to the opposite reality. Because these companies are so big, quality assurance and transparency lie outside the public's reach. They bury problems under layers of bureaucracy. Issues are allowed to fester outside the attention of the national media. The whole cancer continues unabated. And it grows.

The federal government outsourced its power to the states to negotiate with the formula companies directly. The federal agencies retain the job of enforcing production standards, but the states negotiate their rebates and welfare programs independently. Each state secures their own contracts with the *Special Supplemental Nutrition Program for Women, Infants, and Children* (known as WIC). Over a million babies depend on this federal benefit program for their food source.[64] Mothers depending on this government system to pay for baby food were previously limited to the brands under contract, until the Sturgis shutdown and shortage forced them to open the reimbursements to any manufacturer that could put formula on the shelves.

This system makes it easier for low-income, vulnerable families to have access to formula, as it intended. But it also makes the underlying drawbacks of the system far worse. Any manufacturer that can't secure a contract with the state struggles to compete in that market. The company that wins the WIC contract often sees the sales of their products triple, when they are eligible for government reimbursement. Even non-rebate products, the ones that the state is not willing to pay for, will see a significant spike in demand. These non-eligible products increase sales by an average of 70%. This is because companies have the best access to eye-level shelf space in stores. They refer to this as the *spillover effect* in their financial reporting. It's a well-documented phenomenon. So, with this tripled income and increased sales of spillover profits, that should make things cheaper and more efficient right?

---

64   *WIC Data Tables.* Food and Nutrition Service U.S. Department of Agriculture. (2022, July 8). Retrieved August 10, 2022, from https://www.fns.usda.gov/pd/wic-program

Not so. A 2004 study from the Department of Agriculture found that when manufacturers win state contracts, their prices actually increase. And the larger the WIC program, the greater the increase in prices. Even non-contract brands increase their prices to keep up with the contract brand. These companies are going after the WIC market, and they know the taxpayer is footing the bill. The report concludes that "A change in the WIC contract brand within a market area regardless of who won or lost the contract, was also associated with a small but statistically significant, effect on the retail prices of some types of formula."[65]

This demonstrates the chilling effect that these policies are having on free market competition. When suppliers compete with one another for customers, they use pricing as a strategy to win business. They drive prices down and work to keep their overhead low and production steady. They install safeguards for their production and supply, in case of a breakdown or recall. When the government is paying for WIC recipients, these companies are no longer beholden to the laws of supply and demand. They can raise prices, banking on the fact that their sales will likely triple by becoming the exclusive provider. They behave as a group, taking advantage of the rising price of the contract brand to increase their own profits.

The same study from the Department of Agriculture looked at ways to drive that cost back down. Their conclusion? "The results of this analysis indicate that increasing the prevalence of breastfeeding among WIC infants would decrease the retail price of both the contract and noncontract brands of infant formula."

This is important. Here is a government report that is admitting that increased rates of breastfeeding would actually decrease the cost

---

65   Prell, M. (2004, December). *An Economic Model of WIC, the Infant Formula Rebate Program, and the Retail Price of Infant Formula.* Food Assistance and Nutrition Research Report Number 39-2. Retrieved August 15, 2022, from https://www.ers.usda.gov/publications

of formula. This is a very important concession in further conversation around the formula and breastfeeding discussion. The lines are drawn, in conclusions like this one. Breastfeeding poses a threat to the profitability of welfare programs like WIC, and by extension, the profitability of the companies who provide the formula at stake.

The research indicates that WIC participants are less likely to successfully breastfeed beyond six months. This is half the time the American Academy of Pediatrics recommends, and one quarter of what the World Health Organization and many international health groups recommend. Just 44% of WIC children are exclusively breastfed through the first month, and at six months, only 4.7% of WIC mothers are breastfeeding. WIC mothers are also more likely to introduce solid foods before six months (what AAP and WHO recommend), and roughly a quarter of WIC mothers did so by 4 months.[66] This parallels the failing six-month exclusive breastfeeding rates from the 1950s, the historic national low.

Non-WIC infants, as of 2004, were being successfully breastfed at a rate of about 44% past their first month. For WIC infants, that number was less than half of that. And today, it's estimated to be around 15-18% success rate for breastfeeding at the six-month mark. These formula manufacturers understand these basic economics. The more children that are successfully breastfed, the smaller the relative size of the WIC program. That has the greatest effect on their sales and prices when they win state contracts. That conclusion was supported by the USDA report as well.

As of 2015, Abbott held WIC contracts in 23 states. As of 2022, Abbott Nutrition runs this program for at least 31 states. In the summer

---

66   Jacknowitz, A., Novillo, D., & Tiehen, L. (2007, February 1). *Special Supplemental Nutrition Program for Women, infants, and children and infant feeding practices.* American Academy of Pediatrics. Retrieved August 15, 2022, from https://publications.aap.org/pediatrics/article-abstract/119/2/281/70305/ Special-Supplemental-Nutrition-Program-for-Women

of 2022, the government decided that the WIC program would pay for any brand of formula. They just had to make it onto the shelves. In some states, only half of companies were able to meet the supply. They presented this to the public as offering more choice to desperate families on fixed or government incomes. Given the situation, though, it will likely only exacerbate the problem of low competition. It's a similar outcome to when the federal government subsidized college tuition. Universities no longer had to charge what their education was worth. They charged what they thought the government was willing to pay for it. Statewide formula prices are doing the same thing as college tuition. For a middle-class family that is not a WIC recipient, prices tend to climb while supply stays low.

Even before implementing the WIC program, though, the market was very concentrated. This means that only three manufacturers controlled 98% of the entire industry. All three of these manufacturers are owned by pharmaceutical companies: Abbott Laboratories owned by Ross Labs, Bristol-Myers owned by Mead Johnson, and Nestlé-Wyeth Nutrition purchased by Pfizer in 2012[67].

Manufacturers know what the states are willing to pay. They understand the inflexibility of their product, meaning it is something that parents will do whatever is necessary to get it. Like defense contractors or vaccine manufacturers, they know Congress must keep their product on the shelf at practically any cost. Even the current shortages have congressional representatives scrambling to budget for a stockpile of aluminum and vegetable oil for future formula production during supply chain slowdowns. One regulatory agency volunteered for this job, asking for an additional $8.4 billion and congressional authority to regulate this. The agency? The beloved

67   Oliveira, V. (2011, September 11). *Winner takes (almost) all: How WIC affects the infant formula market.* USDA ERS - Infant Formula Market. Retrieved September 8, 2022, from https://www.ers.usda.gov/amber-waves/2011/september/infant-formula-market/

FDA, with its gleaming track record of responsible enforcement and efficiency.

The welfare system, even at the state level, is hostage to the formula manufacturer demands and the changing weather of the national supply chain. They can raise their prices because the low-income families are immune to it. Middle-class families not participating in WIC have few or no other options. This industry capitalizes on parents' concerns for feeding their newborns. These companies know parents are willing to pay whatever it takes. This is why, in the height of the formula panic, eight cans of formula were selling on eBay for $800.[68] Parents are being told it's due to the shortage, to supply chain issues due to COVID, and so on. And the so-called upper class? They're breastfeeding their children, statistically.

Please bear in mind that this is not a judgment statement on how mothers are choosing to feed their babies. This is simply pointing out that for WIC mothers who have elected to breastfeed their children, this is an alarming trend that deserves a closer look. It also gives us some historical context to the scope of the problem. Despite all the advances for women's rights in the past half century, as well as civil rights for minority populations, how is it that we have returned to the 1950s levels in terms of outcomes for the empowerment for black mothers to breastfeed their babies? Where is the progress on that statistic?

The infant formula market thrives in the inner city. It particularly caters to single mothers with little to no maternity leave following delivery. Too many of them struggle through pregnancy, often working multiple jobs. After the baby arrives, they rush to return to work, having exhausted their sick leave and savings account, and

---

68   Swenson, K., & Portnoy, J. (2022, May 13). *U.S. baby formula shortage leaves parents scrambling.* The Washington Post. Retrieved August 21, 2022, from https://www.washingtonpost.com/dc-md-va/2022/05/11/formula-shortage-parents-inflation/

breastfeeding simply is not an option. No maternity leave exists. Family members or other care providers have no option but to formula feed, as mom returns to the rat race far too soon after baby's arrival. Natural law, as mentioned previously, requires a provider and a nurturer, and when mother cannot be the nurturer, when she is forced to provide. The government and their friends in the formula industry will step in to replace the mother as an increasingly failed substitute for her presence and breastmilk.

There is a strong push to attempt to legislate away the consequences of this natural law. An increased demand for mothers to stay home as the nurturer, demanding that the government replace the father instead. While this may address some of the short-term concerns, it is unlikely to address the deeper, systemic issues that contribute to the problem of starving babies.

The United States is the only developed nation in the world without legislated maternity leave. In fact, only six other nations do not offer such protection, and all are island countries in the Pacific: the Marshall Islands, the Federated States of Micronesia, Nauru, Palau, Papua New Guinea, and Tonga.[69] Establishing paid maternity leave was one of the key goals of the Biden Administration, but Democrats abandoned efforts during the budget talks of 2021.[70] Case law precedent in this country does not recognize any official connection between pregnancy and lactation. While an employer cannot legally dismiss a woman for pregnancy under the Civil Rights Act, there is no extension of this protection if she chooses to breastfeed her child while employed.

69   Rupp, L. (2021, October 28). *Paid maternity leave by country: Only 5 places are as stingy as U.S.* Bloomberg.com. Retrieved September 20, 2022, from https://www.bloomberg.com/news/articles/2021-10-28/paid-family-leave-how-much-does-us-offer-compared-to-other-countries?leadSource=uverify+wall
70   Wasson, E. (2021, October 27). *Democrats abandon paid family leave from Biden Economic Plan.* Bloomberg Law. Retrieved September 20, 2022, from https://news.bloomberglaw.com/daily-labor-report/democrats-drop-paid-family-leave-from-biden-economic-plan

SOCIAL AND RACIAL CONSIDERATIONS

The recent Supreme Court ruling on federal abortion laws have shown that many companies are ready and willing to pay for out-of-state abortions. They understand that it is far cheaper and more effective for the company's bottom line for their female employees to undergo an abortion. It takes far more time and energy to support her during pregnancy and lactation. Global quarantines normalized telecommuting for work. Surely employers ought to be able to find some allowances for breastfeeding moms. Mothers can remain productive and contribute to the workplace without leaving their babies. They should not be forced to quarantine themselves, but some accommodations can be made to allow them to be both mothers and contributing team members.

An examination of the data behind this problem is heartbreaking. To illustrate, Black single mothers in the United States have a success rate of exclusively breastfeeding their child at the six-month mark of only 17%. Black infants' breastfeeding success rates are 10-20 percentage points below White infants. The CDC attributes this disparity to five major factors:

1. Black mothers compared to White mothers are more likely to have incomes below the national poverty level (49.3% versus 17.8%).

2. They are WIC recipients (78.2% versus 34.1%).

3. They are single mothers (65.5% versus 23.9%).

4. And there are differences in level of education and the younger age at which they are having babies.

5. The CDC goes on to state that Black mothers experience a higher rate of obstacles to breastfeeding. These include a lack

of knowledge about breastfeeding. They often lack social and healthcare provider support and face employment demands.[71]

Similar difficulty has been documented in Hispanic communities as well. The percentage of mothers attempting to start breastfeeding is similar in Hispanic and White mothers. But Hispanic mothers are failing at a much higher rate than Black mothers regarding how long they choose to breastfeed their babies, and whether they choose to only feed them breastmilk during the first six months of life. This may be due to similar circumstances in both Black and Hispanic minorities. Further research is vital to better help these struggling moms feed their newborns.

Evidence-based maternity care practices are lower among healthcare facilities in predominantly Black neighborhoods. Some of the biggest determining factors for successful feeding are noticeably absent. These are things like receiving lactation consultation within the first hour of the baby's life and avoiding infant formula unless medically indicated.

The high rate of attempted breastfeeding, and the low success rate is the best scenario for the formula industry. This allows them to give a nod to the *breast is best* crowd when in the hospital with newborns, while quietly initiating formula in the privacy of the home. Hospitals correctly feel they have done their best to start breastfeeding with lactation consultation and education. But mothers, particularly minority moms, still convert to the profitable customers that Big Bottle is hoping for.

The logical question follows: If sales for a formula company are driven by WIC participants, why would they ever want anything to change? Why would they improve access to alternatives that are less

71   Beauregard, J. L., Hamner, H. C., Chen, J., Avila-Rodriguez, W., Elam-Evans, L. D., & Perrine, C. G. (2019, August 29). *Racial disparities in breastfeeding initiation and duration among...* Centers for Disease Control and Prevention. Retrieved August 10, 2022, from http://dx.doi.org/10.15585/mmwr.mm6834a3

profitable for the company? If their goal was to keep breastfeeding success rates under 17%, would they do anything different? In communities where WIC programs are the strongest, so too is the influence of these formula companies on social media, pediatrician product placement, and hospital practices affecting breastfeeding rates, particularly with regards to birth interventions.

These companies make a huge show of donating formula for disaster relief. They place their product and bright labels all over the hospitals. They put it in pediatric and obstetric offices everywhere in these communities. These companies also buy lavish gifts, cruises, dinners, and equipment for these providers. They pay for guest speakers and lecturers to go to medical conferences. Their talking points are carefully crafted to keep the current demand up, and breastfeeding success down. Many healthcare providers have previously turned a blind eye to the problem but are waking up to the science and data behind the infant formula crisis. Where they may previously have been quick to recommend supplementation or a switch to exclusive formula feeding, they are beginning to re-examine this paradigm. Those who are adapting their approach, increasing successful breastfeeding rates, are seeing the greatest infant healthcare outcome improvements. They are feeding and reconnecting babies.

If a mother becomes aware of the risks of formula contamination and the lack of true oversight from the federal agencies; if a father realizes that despite all their talk to the contrary, the White House Press Secretary and everyone on down to the local pediatrician is increasingly powerless to help fix a broken system; if these parents decide to leave the system that is no longer serving them, what are their options?

Reversing the formula trend, they begin to explore options like homemade formula, which the FDA and formula makers warn is risky due to contamination and nutrient deficiency. They begin to look at obtaining donor milk on social media, the modern-day equivalent of wet nursing. They explore the option of supplementing with goat milk, an increasingly popular option given its small curd size and absorbability. Finally, they seriously consider a return to breastfeeding.

Instantly, the programming of the formula industry kicks in. Mothers fear being unable to establish or maintain a supply. They are told there are easier options. They are made to feel that their career or their social life will suffer if they are choosing this route. From the moment a mother decides to breastfeed her child, she becomes a direct competitor of a multibillion-dollar cartel. The formula company's simple aim is to convert a new mother into a faithful consumer for the next twelve to twenty-four months. When she chooses to leave their sales funnel, it represents a financial loss for these companies.

If 91% of mothers were able to breastfeed successfully up to 6 months of age, the United States would save an immediate $13 billion annually.[72] Other indirect savings would certainly number much higher. The cost of healthcare would decrease, given the lower incidence of chronic and childhood illnesses. Maybe the system is hesitant to leave such profits on the table.

CONSIDERING ALTERNATIVES WITHOUT SHAME OR PRIVILEGE

A new effort is underway too to shame those who encourage breastfeeding, as some voices claim that advocating breastfeeding can trigger postpartum depression. Some mouthpieces claim the societal pressure on moms to breastfeed is dangerous to her mental health.

---

72   Bartick, M., & Reinhold, A. (2010). The burden of suboptimal breastfeeding in the United States: a pediatric cost analysis. Pediatrics, 125(5), e1048–e1056. https://doi.org/10.1542/peds.2009-1616

One mother recently stated, "I firmly believe my postpartum depression and postpartum anxiety was triggered from the whole breastfeeding experience... There are facilities and 'experts' who are so pro-breastfeeding, that instead of being supportive of breastfeeding," she said, "it almost feels like they're mandating it."[73]

Another mother wrote "I'm still livid about the politics and policies around infant feeding that have turned breastfeeding into a moral imperative and amplified the privilege of those who are able and in a position to do so. I'm still the first to stand up for infant formula as a life-saving product that has done more than any other to advance gender parity in infant feeding through decades that have seen women enter the workforce en masse."[74]

This second voice is that of Leila Strickland, the co-founder and CSO of Biomilq. She appears to be using her new position and her voice to join the formula advertisers telling moms they must choose between a career and motherhood. They can't do it all. It's instilling that doubt that if they choose to breastfeed, they will lose opportunities at work. Unless, of course, these mothers buy her product.

Breastfeeding is not *a moral imperative*. It isn't amplifying privilege. It's a biological building block, and the healthiest babies, based on the available studies, evidence, and statistics, are those that are fed exclusively via the breast from birth to six months of age. Mothers are intelligent enough to entertain this discussion without being made to feel like victims of a patriarchy that wants to enforce breastfeeding. They can weigh the options without being guilted about their ultimate choice or feeling attacked by the science of the issue. Parents are

73   Pearson, C. (2020, July 30). *The pressure to breastfeed can hurt women. and doctors are finally realizing it*. HuffPost. Retrieved August 21, 2022, from https://www.huffpost.com/entry/breastfeeding-pressure-women-mental-health-doctor_l_5d811672e4b00d69059fc2d0

74   Strickland, L. (2021, October 19). *Happy birthday BIOMILQ: A reflection by Leila Strickland, our CSO & Co-founder*. BIOMILQ. Retrieved September 20, 2022, from https://www.biomilq.com/post/happy-birthday-biomilq-a-reflection-by-leila-strickland-our-cso-co-founder

hungry for the facts, they are free to choose, and they are ready to put their babies ahead of every other societal consideration.

The recommendation to breastfeed is not nearly as forceful as the advertising to formula feed. If it were, more mothers would choose to exclusively breastfeed. However, such unintended pressure comes from zealous providers who may be out of touch with their patients' needs. Their insistence on the supremacy of breastfeeding overshadows other factors. Breastfeeding is not mandatory, but current data overwhelmingly shows how superior it is to formula alternatives.

The message and approach can be different, for mothers who feel so pressured. The ideal destination should remain the same, however: healthy, well-fed infants and a happy mother who is confident in her maternal role for that child. This scenario requires some examination of the narrative and some genuine human connection. Doctors and nurses should never apologize for sharing uncomfortable truths if it saves or improves a baby's life. But that truth requires a foundation of trust and communication that allows them to do so without coming across as pushy or overbearing. Why are they not seen as "pushy" if it comes to recommending supplemental or exclusive formula feeding? When breastfeeding is discussed, they are quickly painted as overbearing medical patriarchs.

There are consequences to reinventing the natural system, especially when science is only now beginning to scratch the surface of breastmilk's ingredients. The more research uncovers, the more providers realize exactly what this white gold represents. It can't be fabricated. It can't be mass produced. And even assuming milk scientists could successfully counterfeit this nutrient, babies would miss out on the miracle that is in the delivery. A future chapter in this book will discuss this process, one of the most remarkable phenomena in the natural world. There are incredible benefits for both mother and baby that are forfeited too readily.

Pointing out these long-established and evidence-based benefits is not shaming mothers who choose to feed their babies differently, or who are unable to establish and maintain their own milk supply. While acknowledging that sometimes breastfeeding is not possible for many reasons, those who affirm it is the best possible outcome can do so without judging or shaming mothers. They are speaking based on facts, following the historic and natural pattern that has kept babies alive and nourished for millennia. As evidenced by the history of the infant formula industry, science hasn't always known what it does now. It has been a story of progress, of some failures and setbacks, but overall, of resilience and adaptation. Mothers have always worked to find a way to feed their babies.

Our current trajectory is concerning. The United States currently faces the highest infant mortality rate of the top twenty wealthiest countries in the world.[75] The need for improving infant outcomes is matched only by the importance of suspending judgment and preserving medical choice. Guilting and shaming mothers who decide differently on these matters is not helpful. Some reach their conclusion by choice, but some are out of necessity. Each reaches it after serious thought and concern for their baby. Motherhood must be a bond that connects, and not a wall that divides or a pedestal from which to lecture others. There are myriad reasons and circumstances for every family's decision on whether to breastfeed.

Formula companies have also managed to infiltrate medical schools and nursing programs. Conversations like the one regarding

---

75   Thakrar, A. P., Forrest, A. D., Maltenfort, M. G., & Forrest, C. B. (2018, January 1). *Child mortality in the US and 19 OECD comparator nations: A 50-year time-trend analysis: Health Affairs Journal*. Health Affairs. Retrieved August 10, 2022, from https://www.healthaffairs.org/doi/10.1377/hlthaff.2017.0767

breastfeeding and post-partum mental health are becoming more popular, with less data and more emotion driving the results.

Formula makers know that if mothers give their babies formula in the hospital, that triples the odds of them being formula fed by two months. The American Academy of Pediatrics tracked 5,310 WIC babies in Minnesota. They failed at breastfeeding six times more than babies who were not fed formula in the hospital.[76] Research shows that these practices regarding formula feeding are reducing the success rates of breastfeeding. What is being done to address the matter?

THE INTERNATIONAL CODE FOR BREASTFEEDING

Formula companies understand these dynamics well. They have been hard at work to enshrine their procedures in place, even from this early phase. As discussed earlier, any "helpful lists" of things to pack when you're expecting will remind mom to bring her "formula and baby bottles" with her to the hospital. These companies are expecting her to fail at feeding. They want to ensure their formula is easily accessible in her overnight bag when that happens. Data shows that's what she reaches for at two in the morning with a screaming child.

And if that isn't enough, they want to send free gifts to mom. They supply the hospital with copious amounts of their product. It's specially labeled for "newborns". This is in direct violation of the International Code for Breastfeeding, or simply *The Code*, which was adopted by the World Health Organization since 1981.

Since The Code passed, 135 participating countries have agreed upon certain standards. They have adopted guidelines for advertising and marketing formula. They have methods of production and research. They have worked to legislate these measures into practice in

---

76   McCoy, M. B., & Heggie, P. (2020, July 1). *In-hospital formula feeding and breastfeeding duration.* American Academy of Pediatrics. Retrieved August 15, 2022, from https://doi.org/10.1542/peds.2019-2946

their respective nations. There are 49 countries with no legal measures in place who do not participate in The Code. One of these countries is the United States.[77]

In countries participating in The Code, hospitals are forbidden from "gifting" of formula. These companies through hospital intermediaries gamble the first round of formula. They know that it will spark the process that will secure a lifelong customer. Baby will experience their first physiological substance addiction. Mom will become hooked on the ease, convenience, and perception of independence she craves. If they can't get her to abandon breastfeeding exclusively from the beginning, perhaps having a small sample packet can encourage her to "top off" her feedings. This confuses her body, whose entire supply is driven by the infant demand.

Many US hospitals send parents home with gift bags, violating The Code and all the standards of "baby friendly" hospitals the world over. Formula is a common gift at a baby shower, a raffle drawing at community events, and a staple in food banks and donation centers nationwide. The intentions can be the most pure and supportive in the world. The effects are the same: insulin resistance, digestive tract damage, and separation of mother's instinct to feed from baby's need to be fed. Enter the formula maker, the unwanted wet nurse.

One of the biggest efforts of the WHO is to reduce direct-to-consumer marketing of "newborn formula." Following the logic of the World Health Organization, both the American Academy of Pediatrics and their counterparts in the European Union have affirmed that exclusive breastfeeding until the age of six months is the most evidence-based approach to healthy babies. Therefore, any deviation from this ought to be the concern of a healthcare provider. As such, any intervention for formula feeding or supplementation should fall

---

77   WHO. UNICEF. IBFAN. Marketing of Breast-milk Substitutes: National Implementation of the International Code. Status Report 2016. Geneva: World Health Organization; 2016.

under the jurisdiction of a medical provider. They should monitor the situation. Think of infant formula for under 6 months old like a medication. So why do we label "newborn" formulas as such?

This is not normal in most of the world. Only the prescribing doctors know the medications they are treating with. It keeps the patients from pressuring the doctors into certain brands. Of course, doctors still disclose the possible side effects as part of the informed consent. This keeps the pharmaceutical companies sidelined from the patient-doctor relationship and conversations.

The World Health Organization has decided that this is also where the formula companies belong too. On the sideline. If a newborn to six-month-old requires formula feeding, it is to be done in an unlabeled bottle. It is not done with the brand fanfare of the American hospitals, where babies are wheeled around on a cart with containers of flashy formulas. Abroad, most stores do not sell "newborn formulas" off the shelf. If any are caught advertising such product lines, they can have their distributorship pulled. They can be required to display signage informing customers that due to their violation of The Code, such product is no longer available from this distributor. It is taken very seriously.

Contrast all this with the United States, where formula companies offer hotlines for struggling mothers to call when they are having breastfeeding issues at home. Any guesses as to what these call centers will recommend? I'll give you a hint: it doesn't involve calling the midwife, pediatric chiropractor, or changing the baby's position for a better latch.

These companies also print and circulate "growth charts" for pediatricians and hospitals. These show moms how quickly their baby should be gaining weight after delivery. Otherwise, they say, it may be time to discuss supplementation or a complete transition to formula and bottle feeding. "You gave it your best," they all seem to say. "But our product is better at feeding your child." These companies sponsor continuing education events. They donate heavily to American Academy of Pediatrics on the state and national levels[78], a huge conflict of interest and violation of The Code for a professional organization charged with being an objective bystander. They have purchased the system from top to bottom. And they understand their environment incredibly well!

Even the tiniest of details have not escaped the attention of the marketing minds at these formula companies. They realized that if they placed the neonatal intensive care units, nurseries, and formula storage areas away from the small delivery rooms on hospital wings, they could more efficiently separate mothers and infants during that formative hour. This gives them the best chance of shutting down her production in favor of theirs. These companies have become adamant about the way this system is to flow. The layout of the hospital is so important to their system, they donate the architectural designs for hospitals. This ensures they maintain this type of control over the delivery wards. These plans are *donated* by the formula giants to ensure that all this happens like clockwork.

They send millions of dollars to medical schools. They fly in guest speakers and pediatric experts to continuing education seminars and professional organizations. Their formula marketing will be front and center. They shower doctors with lavish dinners, with expensive gifts and incentive cruises. They've taken a leaf directly from the playbook of the pharmaceutical companies to pay these legalized bribes. They maintain absolute control of a system designed to make money for the hospital on repeat visits or readmission to babies "failing to thrive", of losing the water weight they gained from the IV at birth. This

78 Rothwell, C. (2019, August 14). *AAP's relationship with Formula companies.* USLCA. Retrieved August 23, 2022, from https://uslca.org/clinical-pearl/aap-and-formula-companies/

further solidifies their access to the consumer, and eventually, their profitability.

That is the mammoth system mothers are up against. It's Cronos, the titan that is devouring the next generation. That's why every opportunity to turn a "no" into a "yes" will be taken. Every call for a nurse in the middle of the night with a baby who refuses to latch is their chance. Every mom new to breastfeeding is greeted with a sympathetic smile and a ready-to-serve bottle from whatever company happens to own that hospital's administration or state formula contract.

Studies also affirm "breastfeeding provides optimal nutrition to infants and provides health benefits for both infants and mothers." It admits that "breastfed infants have reduced risk for ear, respiratory, and gastrointestinal infections and might be less likely to develop asthma, obesity, and diabetes. Mothers who breastfeed have a lower risk for developing type 2 diabetes, hypertension, and breast and ovarian cancers."[79] This is why successful breastfeeding should be a cornerstone of national public health focus.

When an expecting mom gets a list from her doctor of things to bring in her overnight bag, what do they often include? *Don't forget infant formula and bottles.* She hasn't even given birth yet. The formula companies are already betting against her. She hasn't even attempted breastfeeding. Are they so sure she will fail they want her to have a pre-purchased formula supply on-hand and ready to deploy at a moment's notice?

So much is thrown at her. This is the first time a mother is faced with a huge, life-changing event like bringing a baby into the world. She knows enough of the risks to feel fear. She trusts the doctors and

79   Beauregard, J. L., Hamner, H. C., Chen, J., Avila-Rodriguez, W., Elam-Evans, L. D., & Perrine, C. G. (2019, August 29). *Racial disparities in breastfeeding initiation and duration among...* Centers for Disease Control and Prevention. Retrieved August 10, 2022, from http://dx.doi.org/10.15585/mmwr.mm6834a3

nurses enough to feel safe. She may be accompanied by her husband, a parent, or a sibling, but they are there for moral support, not birthing advice. She understands the process well enough to anticipate the next step.

But almost nobody is telling her to trust herself. There are very few voices reminding her she is enough, and she is what this baby needs. The staff leaves, her husband nods off to sleep, and the lights go out. She faces the first wave of self-doubt. In the quiet reflection and darkness, responding to the cries of this tiny new person, she tries to bring her newborn to breast. She's seldom held an infant before, let alone helped it latch. She recalls the hurried consultation with the lactation specialist earlier today. It is all a whirlwind now. *Is this right? She wonders. Does it always hurt this much? Is my baby getting enough? Am I enough?*

FOUR:
THE BENEFITS OF BREASTFEEDING

INITIATION, DURATION, AND EXCLUSIVITY

Nature did not overlook or fail any part of the birth and breastfeeding process. It does not need intervention, supplementation, modification, enhancement, or correction. It simply needs to be trusted, free from interference. When the national approach has been one of constant attempts to replace, improve, or to alter the naturally appointed course, there are always tradeoffs. These tradeoffs carry real-world consequences. Increasingly, these tradeoffs are downplayed, the consequences are minimized or medicated away. The overall trend, however, is the current maternal and infant health breakdown we are witnessing today. On the other hand, if a mother decides that powdered infant formula or human-like milk produced in a lab is not the best option for her newborn, she is likely to return to breastfeeding as the preferred method of feeding her child.

Not only are parents today facing a destabilized food supply of powdered infant formula, but most of them do not realize they are also facing a national shortage of breastmilk. Most new or experienced mothers are focused so heavily on pregnancy and delivery that some of the groundwork for successful breastfeeding is often overlooked.

For any mother who is contemplating a return to breastmilk over powdered formula, this is a prospect worth considering. Many are hesitant due to misunderstanding and misinformation, some of which is intentional, around breastfeeding. The American Academy of Pediatrics recommends breastfeeding up to one year of age. This is half of what the international community recommends. Currently, less than 5% of babies are breastfed by the time they reach their first birthday[80]. What does this really mean, though? What's at stake here?

One reality is increasingly apparent. This is not a decision to be made lightly. It will require dedication and intention, and although it is the most natural and innate thing in the world, so many of the interventions and interferences of modern living have complicated it to the point of overwhelming a new mother. This intimidation can be overcome with support and information. It is entirely possible, but it takes effort and understanding. The benefits far exceed these obstacles, however, and no matter the course this breastfeeding journey takes, there are rewards at every step of the way. There is benefit in every attempt.

83% of new moms attempt to initiate breastfeeding in the hospital. This statistic is encouraging. It shows that more are making the attempt. But by three months of age, less than half of babies still breastfeed. And by six months, that number drops to just one quarter. That's the focus of the current problem. This statistic from the CDC doesn't track data at one year, let alone at two years of age.

When discussing breastfeeding, there are three aspects that researchers consider: initiation, duration, and exclusivity. These terms ensure those who are discussing benefits and outcomes are comparing apples to apples when looking at the research.

---

80   Wolf, J. H. (2011, October 10). *Low breastfeeding rates and public health in the United States.* American Journal of Public Health. Retrieved August 10, 2022, from https://ajph.aphapublications.org/doi/full/10.2105/AJPH.93.12.2000

Initiation means that within one hour of birth, mother is allowing the baby to latch at the breast. There is no supplementation with formula. In hospital births, this is often under the supervision of a lactation specialist. If a baby is preterm, *expressed milk*, meaning milk that is pumped from the breast and bottled for baby, can be used to feed until the infant develops the strength and reflexes for a successful latch. Most mothers will offer the breast ten to twelve times within a twenty-four-hour period. This immediate contact and frequent engagement help remind the body that it is lactating and needs to be renewing the supply. The benefits of conferred immunity, of sharing immune system protection between mother and baby, begin almost immediately.

Duration refers to the length of time in months that a baby is breastfed. The WHO and European Union strongly advocate for two years duration. They have well-researched the developmental benefits to this point. The American Academy of Pediatrics encourages at least one year. Currently, only one in five American babies are reaching six months of exclusive breastfeeding[81]. It's important to note the difference between *any* breastfeeding versus *exclusive* when looking at these types of numbers. Although there are plenty of benefits to certain approaches, most of the data is investigating outcomes in children who are *exclusively* breastfed.

Exclusivity means that baby receives only breastmilk for the first six months, no other liquids or solids, including water. At six months, mother can begin introducing simple, healthy solids, and eventually the child will eat regular toddler foods, all the while continuing to breastfeed. Parents can continue to add foods with the breastmilk to the first (according to the AAP) or second (WHO recommendation) year of life.

---

81   Centers for Disease Control and Prevention. (2022, August 1). *Results: Breastfeeding rates.* Centers for Disease Control and Prevention. Retrieved August 11, 2022, from https://www.cdc.gov/breastfeeding/data/nis_data/results.html

MEDICAL FREEDOM: AN ESSENTIAL HUMAN RIGHT

This topic must be approached from a safe place, and an absolute surrender of judgment or criticism. Medical autonomy is key. *Medical autonomy* refers to the ability to make decisions for oneself and those for whom one has a legal obligation to do so, in this instance a newborn. This freedom does not extend to other parents who may decide differently. It also does not extend to our ability to make choices for our former selves either. Too many mothers judge themselves in the harsh light of what they understand now, rather than extend grace and understanding to the previous self. They didn't know then what we know now. They were doing the best they could at the time with what they knew. Supporting and loving those who choose differently is paramount, even if that person who is choosing differently is our previous selves. Parenthood, especially navigating complex issues like breastfeeding, requires an acknowledgement of the grit and determination this crucial role requires.

In the quest to address starving babies, we need to make a wide enough circle to allow all approaches and attempts in. All carefully considered positions and every expression of personal choice is to be validated and lauded for its valued attempt to provide for and connect with these newborns. Some mothers are forced to rush back to a demanding job simply to make ends meet. Any research into human donor milk or formula alternatives is a valiant effort, but so is the reality of a mom who wants to work hard and feed her child. Some mothers choose to pump and store their supply for their child or for others. They may weigh the odds of the hormonal and immune system benefits against the reality of a situation that is so far below the surface of public opinion, that their efforts to maintain a healthy supply is an undisputed victory. These mothers who are pumping and feeding their little ones do so with all the pressure to formula feed from manufacturers, and too often with judgment from the "breast is best" world. They occupy a middle ground in the two camps, and such division only serves the current status. It is one that is separating, judging, and doubting mothers, and it has no place in a supportive breastfeeding culture.

CREEPING DOUBTS

Many modern American moms are often told they don't have adequate supply. They often hear that their milk is nutrient deficient, or their baby is allergic to the supply. If the baby's weight dips, if their latch is off, or they seem hungry, they immediately reach for formula. These doubts make their way in early on. They usually come from very well-meaning sources, and people who have chosen a different path and are looking to feel supported and validated in their own journeys. That is a different route, the factors surrounding that baby were unique to them, and their body is completely separate and individual. Comparison and standardization are not helpful to parents who are looking to change the current paradigm.

The belief that a baby is not getting enough from milk alone is the biggest factor in the decision to wean that baby at any age.[82] Many moms are worried their baby isn't consuming enough breastmilk, or that the breastmilk is nutritionally defective or inflammatory, or that their child is hungry. Many new mothers wait for their "milk supply to come in" and are constantly concerned that they aren't producing enough. The baby's stomach is tiny, roughly the size of a cherry initially, and it is consuming one of the most nutrient-dense substances. It doesn't require a huge transfer of breastmilk to provide enough, and

---

82   Li, R., Fein, S. B., Chen, J., & Grummer-Strawn, L. M. (2008, October). *Why mothers stop breastfeeding: Mothers' self-reported reasons for stopping during the first year.* Pediatrics. Retrieved August 11, 2022, from https://pubmed.ncbi.nlm.nih.gov/18829834/

with such limited stomach storage space, small feedings often are perfectly adequate.

This is evidence for how far confidence in nature is being undermined by conformity to the current climate. The research simply does not support these notions. A tiny percentage of mothers, likely less than 5%, but data is scarce, are medically, physiologically incapable of producing breastmilk after building an entire human baby. This is incredibly rare. Mothers can build a human and sustain it, if they choose. But that message is not getting through. Doubt and discouragement are the cultural norm far too often.

With the renewed and continued emphasis on breastfeeding, thankfully a greater number of parents and evidence-based birth workers are placing renewed attention on initiation within an hour of birth. However, for mothers who are "boots on the ground", something is happening that is impeding the fulfillment of their desire to breastfeed exclusively.

This book is not an exhaustive manual on breastfeeding. There are far more robust resources out there for mothers who are facing challenges. Lactation consultants and other qualified professionals are excellent sources of information. Instead, this chapter explores the philosophy with which mothers approach breastfeeding before baby is here and seeks to empower them with the benefits of choosing the be their own source of infant nutrition. There are many reasons they are often told they can't, but it only requires one valid reassurance that they can.

FINDING THE "WHY"

First, parents need to understand the motivation for succeeding. They need to establish a "why". For every mother and father, that "why" is their new baby. Why, then, are so many parents set up to fail? It's not that they love their child any less. Many wish they could breastfeed. Their "why" is just as valid as the mother who succeeds at exclusive breastfeeding. They may not understand the obstacles to establish and maintain a healthy milk supply. They may not know the benefits of doing so. They may not yet realize the power of breastfeeding.

Second to this understanding is preparation by eliminating toxins that shut down breastmilk production. The modern environment is awash with many such chemicals. This molecular communication is necessary for a healthy body to build and sustain a separate human. This communication pathway must be clear and calm. It needs to feel safe and competent. It needs to be used. The modern environment shuts down breastmilk production, and this will target some ways to secure it. The human body detoxifies itself constantly and efficiently. This process can be supported by reducing the toxic load and maintaining its inherent cleansing ability.

And third, we need to return to birthing and breastfeeding practices as nature intended. These systems served previous generations of healthy, safe deliveries. Despite spending two and a half times more money per person than the average of comparable nations, the United States is the only country where the maternal mortality rate is actually rising. At a time when the global mortality rate is falling by 43%, the United States saw a two percent increase from 1990 to 2015. This places them 46th in the developed world for maternal health.[83] And number one in spending.

Previous physicians and parents trusted in the power of birth and the body long before formula companies and delivery rooms came along. Cesarean rates were not nearly as common as they are today. Once practitioners and parents alike begin to rediscover how elegant

83   Korbatov, A. B., & De Souza, R.-M. (2015, November 19). *What explains the United States' dismal maternal mortality rates?* Wilson Center. Retrieved September 27, 2022, from https://www. wilsoncenter.org/event/what-explains-the-united-states-dismal-maternal-mortality-rates

and powerful nature's systems are, they return to that confidence that served them well in decades past, when mortality rates were lower, and birth outcomes much better. Those systems fostered connection between mother and child. Connection focused on three vital areas that are too often neglected in the modern approach to birth: nutritional, immunological, and neurological.

The primary messaging mothers face today is very heavy on prenatal and pregnancy up to and including the point of delivery. But many may not be sufficiently prepared for post-partum life and the transition to successful breastfeeding. The healthiest pregnancies begin before conception. Breastfeeding should be just as included in those discussion and preparations. If more mothers understood what was at stake for their child's long-term health, they would be very hesitant to accept any alternative. They would exhaust all other options completely.

The current system pays sufficient lip service to the "breast is best" paradigm. After a wink and a nod from the formula industry, though, too many providers rush in with supplementation or total replacement. They are quick to offer free samples or easy explanations of nutritional adequacy. They enjoy cultural, medical, and pharmaceutical authority, but it has been designed to serve the interests of the formula makers. This is how the industry has successfully medicalized and by so doing, capitalized, on the first and most fundamental nutritional process on planet Earth. This sets them up as the sole and exclusive providers of health for these newborns. When this system sputters to a halt over contamination or quarantine, it doesn't bounce back well. It is designed to run at one speed.

Parents no longer have to rely on that system. They can choose to say "no thank you" and begin their own plan. They don't have to be a part of that philosophy. It's admittedly not easy, but so much of that is by design. These companies want to make it hard to leave the utopia of intervention and dependence. Their way is built on convenience and the illusion of security. But clinical outcomes show their approach is making children sicker and weaker. Change is needed.

This is the biggest paradigm shift parents can make. Most moms are simply not in a position to undertake such a commitment. Too many dads don't understand it. Often, they both have jobs to return to. They suffer pre-existing medical conditions that require medications or interventions that preclude breastfeeding. They have a host of other factors to consider. This all must be acknowledged in order to be addressed. Most parents have also been so carefully conditioned to expect something external to change.

RECLAIMING CONTROL AND ESTABLISHING A PLAN

The increased call for government to mandate employers provide paid maternity and paternity leave is one example of waiting for something external to change. The expectation is that the government will provide free formula to families. Many want formula companies to supply it to hospitals and pediatricians, especially in the case of shortages. This continual passing of the buck that enriches formula manufacturers and empowers government all at the expense of the taxpayer. These external forces are unprepared to step into the responsibility and to capably advocate for hungry babies in the same way that parents can and are willing to do so. They are uniquely qualified to take back the decision making over this portion of nature, if they decide to claim that power.

The factors that truly lie within their control are few. But they are powerful. They are individual. Nobody can dictate the birth and breastfeeding journey. It is as unique as every family's story leading up to it. Providing some background and truth in the face of this propaganda and government passivity empowers that process. As parents are more informed, they realize that more lies in their power to influence than the formula lobby and the birth businesses would have you believe.

There are tremendous benefits to breastfeeding. These are still far too often underutilized by the current medical model despite their own research that affirms it. It is brushed aside too readily, and formula is considered far too equal to breastmilk. As mentioned in an earlier chapter, the content and concentration of DHA and arachidonic acid supplementation in infant formula is just one example of this. When parents truly understand these benefits, they will hesitate to casually forfeit them by filling a bottle with powder and water. They will do everything in their power to prepare for and persevere to provide for their babies.

The research is constantly being re-evaluated, but it has withstood the test of time. The fundamental truth is not changing; breastmilk is the safest, most effective way to nourish a baby. The evidence is constantly being challenged on any alternative to this truth. These are hotly debated among scientists. Those are always being updated and changed with regards to formulas, illnesses, deficiencies, risks, and tradeoffs. If the pharma-formula lobby could poke holes in the core truth of "breast is best", they would. Instead, their representatives pay token lip service to it before telling mothers all the reasons they are exempt from it. They encourage initiation in the hospital, and then somewhere along the way, they redirect them back to the formula system. Those exemptions are now the rule in the overwhelming majority of this country.

We must acknowledge the mother who wishes with everything in her to be able to feed and nourish her tiny human. It requires a sincere effort to reach out and rally in support. Our society must collectively acknowledge the bravery of her journey. We must mourn her losses alongside her. We celebrate her joys. There are solutions in here that every mother is capable of deploying for lasting and meaningful connection and nourishment. Regardless of your choice or circumstance on the matter of breastfeeding the world needs her voice and her heart. While the research around this important topic is presented in a heavily breastfeeding-centric way, this is simply because the pendulum and the culture has moved so far away from it. It is not to shame, demean, or guilt any courageous mother who chooses or is forced to feed differently. Her sacrifices are no less valid, her contributions to her growing child are no less magnificent because the current system has failed her or discarded her desires.

NUTRITION

Breastmilk is sufficient for a baby's constantly adapting needs during the first six months of life. Since nutritional needs evolve daily and even hourly, a mother's body in its infinite wisdom detects and responds to these needs. This happens via the latch at the breast. Her body needs contact and feedback with the infant's in order to change its chemical and microbial makeup when baby latches directly to breast. It can provide perfectly what the growing baby requires. This is a technology that, despite all our advances and attempts, we have only started to understand. To believe it can be replaced by a can of powder or a Petrie dish full of mammary cells is missing the miracle.

Immediately following birth, *colostrum* is produced. This thick, often yellowish milk is high in protein, low in sugar, and packed with essential nutrients. It simply can't be copied by formula. It's crucial in the development of the digestive tract. It initiates many critical processes in preparing babies to process milk. As the baby grows, so will the amount and supply of milk.

Colostrum also has a laxative effect in the baby's intestines. A thick, dark stool called *meconium* forms during gestation. It is supposed to be expelled after delivery. This process coincides with the time that the baby's body is shedding excess *bilirubin*, one of the waste products from the breakdown of blood cells. This is part of the natural process as baby begins to establish blood supply independent from mom.

When bilirubin levels are elevated, babies can become *jaundiced*, and that yellow coloration remains in the tissues, especially in the eyes. Early clearance of the meconium has been shown to reduce the frequency of jaundice and help bilirubin levels normalize. Colostrum promotes the elimination of the meconium, and with it, high levels of bilirubin. This first milk produced around the time of delivery is engineered to coat the gastrointestinal system in prebiotics and probiotics. It has been shown to lower blood pressure[84] and regulate blood sugar[85]. It is there to prepare a brand-new body to absorb all that it needs from the milk for the next six months.

Most humans are Vitamin D deficient. We often hear that breastmilk has insufficient amounts of this key nutrient. Many providers will recommend supplementing with Vitamin D drops. Imagine how much better it would be for mother and baby to fix the primary insufficiency. Parents can ensure they are exposed to healthy amounts of sunlight and a balanced diet. They can monitor Vitamin D levels prior to and during pregnancy. This has tremendous benefits for mom's immune system, as well as baby's developing body. Vitamin D is a critical signaling hormone for a host of processes.

---

84   American Heart Association. (2021, July 21). *Breastfeeding, even for a few days, linked to lower blood pressure in early childhood*. ScienceDaily. Retrieved August 11, 2022, from https://www.sciencedaily.com/releases/2021/07/210721102422.htm

85   *Low blood sugar in the newborn baby*. International BreastFeeding Centre. (2009, July). Retrieved August 11, 2022, from https://ibconline.ca/information-sheets/hypoglycaemia-of-the-newborn-low-blood-sugar/

Mothers planning to breastfeed approach prenatal preparation, pregnancy, and postpartum nutrition differently. They go beyond simply adding a daily multi-vitamin. They choose a lifestyle that includes diet, sleep, sunning, and exercise. These are all intended to help the body process key ingredients to support a strong milk supply when baby arrives.

ANTIBODIES and COVID-19

When a baby's immune system forms, it has no direct contact with the outside world. It isn't touching doorknobs and cellphones to learn what germs are helpful or harmful. Only a handful of pathogens are capable of crossing the *placental barrier*, the protective system that protects the womb from the outside world. Nature didn't leave developing humans defenseless. It didn't overlook the immune system of newborns. One would think that a completely inexperienced immune system not even exposed to air can do little to defend itself. So how does it recognize or respond to foreign, invading pathogens? This intelligence comes from mother's immune system.

Updates to the immune system happen every minute of every day. Every surface mother touches, every person she talks to, every breath she takes, she is constantly ingesting particles of pathogens. And how glorious that process is! These would-be killers are routed into tonsils and adenoids, like the body's immigration and customs control. Specialized cells interrogate threats, blasting them with whatever molecular weapon is most effective. The body learns. It begins to recognize patterns. It discovers the weakness in the microscopic autopsies it conducts of these invading germs. So many mothers are facing weakened and inexperienced immune systems, due to recent quarantine, masking, and mass-sanitization. These measures cut off the exposure and feedback process that is the foundation of how the immune system is designed to work.

One tiny part of the body's response to disease are known as antibodies. Antibodies are trophies the body wins from a fight with a disease. It's a tiny genetic library of how to defeat the enemy. It has the battle plan for every sickness mother is winning. And she's sharing that knowledge with her tiny human inside. She provides all the antibodies via the shared bloodstream to prime this little system to fight when it enters the outside world. It is time to empower mothers and fathers everywhere with restored confidence in the human immune system. Parents are and must remain the ultimate decision-makers for their children. They are often forced to step into this role as brand-new parents, advocating for unborn or minutes-old children. Some 7.2 million of them chose to accept this brave role during the worldwide shutdown of COVID-19.[86]

Specialized cells called *lymphocytes* produce these antibodies. When milk production occurs, mammary glands signal these lymphocytes to set up shop in the breast tissue. They begin to generate thousands of antibodies every second. These antibodies are too big to pass into breastmilk, but special receptors on the milk ducts package them and deliver them into the milk supply. The presence of antibodies in the bloodstream or in breastmilk supply can often indicate a resistance or immunity to a certain disease, but not always. As immunology develops and further research is conducted, scientists are beginning to realize that antibodies are not the gold-standard they once thought they were. Sometimes the immune system is operating just fine without antibodies. They are, however, important indicators of conferred immunity and shared protection against certain diseases.

---

86   Osterman , M. J. K., Hamilton, B. E., Martin, J. A., Driscoll, A. K., & Valenzuela, C. P. (2022, February 7). *National Vital Statistics reports - Centers for Disease Control and ...* https://www.cdc.gov/nchs/products/index.htm. Retrieved August 9, 2022, from https://www.cdc.gov/nchs/data/nvsr/nvsr70/NVSR70-17.pdf

During the first six months of exclusive breastfeeding, breastmilk is packed with these antibodies. These help the baby fight off viruses and bacteria. Most of these invaders begin by attacking the mucosa: the eyes, nose, throat, and digestive system. These structures are best equipped to absorb and utilize food and oxygen. They also become the entry point of choice for germs. Nature has developed a substance called *Immunoglobulin A* (IgA) and a whole library of other antibodies in the breastmilk. IgA coats the eyese, nose, throat, and digestive tract with a protective layer in the form of breastmilk. Colostrum is filled with this IgA. This is a genius delivery method for the antibodies. It puts them on the exact structures that need them the most for protection. As a baby nurses, the milk enters their nose, sinuses, throat, even leaks into the tubes of the ears where ear infections might lurk. All these places are awash in antibodies and protective IgA. It's a microscopic army on standby.

When babies are formula fed, this IgA is missing, and with it, the defense against these infectious pathogens. Now these structures are coated with cheap sugars and vitamins, like bait for passing germs waiting for an opportunity to set up shop. There are many studies that show as one paper concludes "strong positive association between the intake of formula and/or non-breastmilk supplements and the risk of hospitalization for infectious causes."[87] Breastfed babies have a reduced risk of hospitalization for infectious causes. This is something no formula, even lab-cultured breastmilk, will ever replicate.

During the height of COVID-19, the decision to separate mothers and infants was especially tragic for this reason. There was no shared immunity occurring. The World Health Organization advised repeatedly "mothers should continue to share a room with their babies

---

87   Hengstermann, S., Mantaring, J. B. V., Sobel, H. L., Borja, V. E., Basilio, J., Iellamo, A. D., & Nyunt-U, S. (2009, September 16). *Formula feeding is associated with increased hospital admissions due to...* Journal of Human Lactation. Retrieved August 11, 2022, from https://journals.sagepub.com/doi/10.1177/0890334409344078

from birth and be able to breastfeed... even when COVID-19 infections are suspected or confirmed..."[88]

Studies repeatedly showed no symptoms or mild symptoms from COVID-19 in infected newborns, with low risk of neonatal death. The worst-case scenario, assuming 100% transmission rate "would result in 1,950 neonatal deaths from COVID-19", reports a groundbreaking report in the Lancet. We lost far more than that, due to the horrendous policy that quarantined babies from the specter of COVID-19. How many? "125,680 neonatal lives could be saved...Policymakers and healthcare professionals need to protect services and ensure clearer messaging to keep mothers and newborns together, even if the mother is SARS-CoV-2-positive,"[89] they conclude. Dr. Anshu Banerjee, the WHO's Director for Maternal, Newborn, Child, and Adolescent Health and Aging goes on to say, "Disruptions to essential health services during COVID-19 have severely affected the quality of care provided to some of the most vulnerable babies, and this includes their right to the lifesaving contact they need with their parents."

The pandemic fears created an opportunity for formula suppliers to scoop up new customers. They launched a campaign to convince mothers that breastfeeding would transmit COVID to their babies. Danone India, a major nutrition food manufacturer, specifically facilitates a YouTube channel "VoiceofExperts". It warns mothers to maintain a distance of six feet and stop breastfeeding until they are fever free for seventy-two hours, symptom free for seven days, and have two negative PCR tests. This advice was completely incompatible with

---

88　New research highlights risks of separating newborns from mothers during COVID-19 pandemic. (2021, March 16). *World Health Organization*. Retrieved August 11, 2022, from https://www.who.int/news/item/16-03-2021-new-research-highlights-risks-of-separating-newborns-from-mothers-during-covid-19-pandemic.

89　Minckas, N., Medvedev, M. M., Adejuyigbe, E. A., Brotherton, H., Chellani, H., & Estifanos, E. S. (2021, February 15). *Preterm care during the COVID-19 pandemic: A comparative risk analysis of neonatal deaths averted by kangaroo mother care versus mortality due to SARS-CoV-2 infection.* eClinicalMedicine. Retrieved August 11, 2022, from https://www.thelancet.com/journals/eclinm/article/PIIS2589-5370(21)00013-4/fulltext

the international research and the WHO's advice. It resulted in a public outcry during the pandemic, and some condemnation from public health officials. But similar advice came from the American Academy of Pediatrics, a once widely respected institution. It has been shown to be equally as misguided[90]. This is just one example of how these companies boosted their demand and profits through misinformation. The Danone India channel is still on YouTube. It contains the trite disclaimer that "the views expressed by medical experts in this forum were their own."[91] This legal hopscotch, of bypassing the consequences of misleading advertising while capitalizing on the cultural authority of doctors, continues unabated.

One quarter of health workers in 62 countries during this time did not allow breastfeeding, even by uninfected mothers. That many babies went without the "lifesaving contact" during their most vulnerable and immunologically fragile hours and days.

The United States, tragically, was just such a country. The American Academy of Pediatrics (AAP) issued guidance for physicians that did just the opposite of what the international literature recommends. While the WHO and international scientific studies repeatedly warned otherwise, the AAP said regarding the decision to temporarily separate infants born to mothers with suspected COVID cases, "This recommendation was offered out of an abundance of caution considering the lack of evidence about the risk of vertical transmission before and during delivery, the risk of transmission from mother to baby after birth and the natural history of COVID-19 infection in the newborn." Dr. Mark L. Hudak served as the chair of the Section

90   World Health Organization. (2020, March 13). *Clinical management of severe acute respiratory infection (SARI) when covid-19 disease is suspected: Interim guidance, 13 March 2020.* World Health Organization. Retrieved August 18, 2022, from https://www.who.int/europe/publications/i/item/WHO-2019-nCoV-clinical-2020-4

91   Tulleken, C. van, Wright, C., Brown, A., McCoy, D., & Costello, A. (2020, October 24). Marketing of Breastmilk Substitutes During the COVID-19 Pandemic. https://doi.org/10.1016/S0140-6736(20)32119-X. Retrieved August 10, 2022, from https://www.thelancet.com/journals/lancet/article/PIIS0140-6736(20)32119-X/fulltext

on Neonatal-Perinatal Medicine for the AAP during this time. "As information develops, it is possible, in fact probable, that some of these initial recommendations will be modified,"[92] Dr. Hudak stated. They were modified. And rightfully so. But far too late for over 100,000 babies. Even as the decision was being made in our country, the preponderance of data and conflicting information had taken shape internationally. It was ignored by American decision-makers.

Did anyone at the American Academy of Pediatrics consider the effects of immediate separation of infant and mother, not just physiologically, but immunologically? *The Lancet* article did. *The British Medical Journal* did. They estimated that keeping mothers and babies (especially preterm infants) together reduced infant death by as much as 40%. It lowered hypothermia deaths by 70%. And it reduced severe infections by 65%[47]. In the middle of a pandemic, that was the trade-off the AAP made. They deemed that an acceptable risk to prevent "vertical transmission", something that did not materialize in the data before or since.

Breastmilk has never been documented to be a primary carrier of COVID-19 infection. Nature protects that supply from pathogens. These hospitals were separating newborns and placing them in temperature controlled isolettes. They were testing them at twenty-four and forty-eight hours old. If they couldn't test them, they isolated them for fourteen days away from mother. Mother and baby shared a blood supply just moments ago, but now they had to be six feet from anyone until mom had no fever for three days. For a baby that had depended on that connection for survival inside the mother, six feet may as well be six lightyears.

And a fever, incidentally, is a known side-effect of epidurals during delivery in a substantial portion of the population. They resolve

92   Downey, K. (2020, April 8). *AAP recommends temporarily separating newborns from mothers with covid-19.* Healio. Retrieved August 11, 2022, from https://www.healio.com/news/pediatrics/20200408/aap-recommends-temporarily-separating-newborns-from-mothers-with-covid19

spontaneously within a few hours in 90% of cases[93], and are not necessarily indicative of an active viral infection like COVID-19. Yet their policies disconnected, isolated, quarantined, and separated these newborns. And they did it "out of an abundance of caution", and in flagrant disregard for the scientific consensus in the rest of the world.

One study found that when preterm babies are separated from mother, 92% of them face elevated heart and respiratory rates. With mom, with skin-to-skin contact, it's just 17%. Separated, they have lower blood sugar levels. Moms have higher measured stress hormone levels. *The Royal College of Obstetricians and Gynecologists* states "Isolation is a significant stressor for infants; for those infants already infected with SARS-CoV-2, isolation could worsen the disease course."[94]

The chief of newborn pediatrics at Pennsylvania Hospital, Dr. Karen M. Puopolo said later "At the beginning of the pandemic, the only data available came from China, where the universal approach was to immediately separate all newborns from the infected mother and isolate them for 14 days. After months of national and international experience with newborns born to mothers who have tested positive... no published report has identified an infant who has died during the initial birth hospitalization as a direct result of SARS-CoV-2 infection."

"We had some heartbreaking cases of mothers who were very ill and delivered prematurely to save their life," she said. "They got better, and they were not allowed to see their premature infant for weeks at a time, because the guidance from CDC was that you needed to test negative twice before you could assume that you are safe to be not contagious. All of that has changed as we've gotten better science and better data in."[95]

93   Gonen, R., Korobochka, R., Degani, S., & Gaitini, L. (2000). Association between epidural analgesia and intrapartum fever. American journal of perinatology, 17(3), 127–130. https://doi.org/10.1055/s-2000-9283
94   Stuebe A. (2020). Should Infants Be Separated from Mothers with COVID-19? First, Do No Harm. Breastfeeding medicine : the official journal of the Academy of Breastfeeding Medicine, 15(5), 351–352. https://doi.org/10.1089/bfm.2020.29153.ams
95   Downey, K. (2020, July 28). *Aap no longer recommends separating newborns from mothers with*

Except we had better data. Our self-proclaimed experts made a conscious and concerted decision to disregard it. We "erred on the side of caution" and we made all these decisions out of an abundance of caution. That caution cost us dearly. It cost lives. The first charge of a doctor is to "do no harm." And while every piece of evidence was suggesting separation was harming our babies, they did it anyway. While formula companies were running deceptive videos on newborn isolation, the international birth community condemned them. The American medical system embraced such misinformation. They enshrined it. They were ostracized by much of the world health community over such decisions, as they rightfully should have been. We can follow the money to see what companies own the mouthpieces of these agencies and organizations. Pharmaceutical companies and formula makers donated to so many foundations, and when the money came in, the science went out.

Bonding and breastfeeding are lifesaving. The willingness of some agencies and organizations to abandon the evidence we have for that was alarming. That unknown and as-of-then unsubstantiated fear of COVID-19 transmission was allowed to undermine the protective and fortifying benefits of connection and breastfeeding. The AAP and CDC in essence, sacrificed known benefits to mitigate unknown risks without accounting for the tradeoff. And this illogical thinking will likely continue until mothers and fathers decide otherwise. Many mothers saw the writing on the wall as they courageously prepared for birth during a pandemic. They made arrangements with their birth team, with their obstetricians. Many opted for a home birth or birth center delivery. They bypassed a system that did not serve their philosophy and that disregarded their wishes. They did so in the face of tremendous pressure and opposition, from judgmental stares and

covid-19. Healio. Retrieved August 11, 2022, from https://www.healio.com/news/pediatrics/20200728/aap-no-longer-recommends-separating-newborns-from-mothers-with-covid19 comments from behind muffled masks. But their strength in birth prevailed, and their babies stand as a testament to the resilience of the connection between mother and baby from birth and beyond.

REDUCED RISK OF DISEASES

Breastfeeding provides huge benefits for the most common illnesses and infections plaguing newborns today.

Infections – A study of over 1200 children by the peer-reviewed medical journal *Pediatrics*, published by the AAP, looked at the amount of breastmilk consumed in the first six months of life. They found strong evidence that breastfeeding for just half the recommended duration lowered the rate of respiratory tract, ear, throat, sinus, lung, and urinary infections by age six years old.[96] Breastmilk supplies incredibly strong antibodies that kill bacteria in these areas. It keeps tissues strong and hydrated, a natural barrier against invading pathogens.

Digestive Health – Breastfeeding promotes lots of different bacteria in the gut. This means that if an invading germ attacks a certain type of bacteria, others take its place. These take up space in the intestinal wall and prevent dangerous cultures from setting themselves up. When healthy, friendly bacteria cover the gut and control resources, a process called "microbial inhibition", babies have stronger stomachs and can better avoid gut issues. This can also protect against Crohn's Disease and ulcerative colitis.[97]

Intestinal Tissue Damage – Feeding premature babies is often done through a nasal or G-tube. This is used when they are too

96   Li, R., Dee, D., Li, C. M., Hoffman, H. J., & Grummer-Strawn, L. M. (2014). Breastfeeding and risk of infections at 6 years. Pediatrics, 134 Suppl 1(Suppl 1), S13–S20. https://doi.org/10.1542/peds.2014-0646D

97   Xu L, Lochhead P, Ko Y, Claggett B, Leong RW, Ananthakrishnan AN. Systematic review with meta-analysis: breastfeeding and the risk of Crohn's disease and ulcerative colitis. Aliment Pharmacol Ther. 2017 Nov;46(9):780-789. doi: 10.1111/apt.14291. Epub 2017 Sep 11. PMID: 28892171; PMCID: PMC5688338.

weak or have not developed the necessary reflexes for feeding by mouth. This poses unique hazards and opportunities for infections, one in particular, *necrotizing enterocolitis*, is particularly associated with tube feeding. However, premature babies that are fed breastmilk exclusively (either mother's supply or a donor's) see far fewer infections.[98] Even with prematurely delivered babies, mother can still express and bottle her own milk supply or obtain a donor's supply to provide the immune benefits inherent to breastmilk during this crucial period.

Reduced Incidence of SIDS – Another peer-reviewed article in Pediatrics concluded that "Breastfeeding is protective against SIDS, and this effect is stronger when breastfeeding is exclusive. The recommendation to breastfeed infants should be included with other SIDS risk-reduction messages to both reduce the risk of SIDS and promote breastfeeding for its many other infant and maternal health benefits."[99] Sudden infant death is a terrifying prospect to any parent and knowing that exclusive breastfeeding reduces this likelihood would be reason enough for most parents to strive for exclusive, prolonged breastfeeding.

Lowered Incidence of Autoimmune Diseases – Breastfeeding leads to a decreased risk of asthma, allergies, eczema, and other chronic auto-immune and inflammatory disorders. As we learn more about the role of the gut in our immune system's health, the link between our intestinal bacteria and our immune system becomes much more of a focus of research. One study found that "the potential of breastmilk to alter the offspring's early gut microbiota is a promising tool for immune education and allergy

---

98   Patel AL, Kim JH. Human milk and necrotizing enterocolitis. Semin Pediatr Surg. 2018 Feb;27(1):34-38. doi: 10.1053/j.sempedsurg.2017.11.007. Epub 2017 Nov 6. PMID: 29275815.

99   Hauck FR, Thompson JM, Tanabe KO, Moon RY, Vennemann MM. Breastfeeding and reduced risk of sudden infant death syndrome: a meta-analysis. Pediatrics. 2011 Jul;128(1):103-10. doi: 10.1542/peds.2010-3000. Epub 2011 Jun 13. PMID: 21669892.

prevention."[100] Considering that the greatest concentration of our serotonin receptors are in our gut, and the more information we have about the gut-brain axis and its bearing on a healthy immune system, this is a huge factor for overall infant health.

Diabetes – an estimated 9% of pregnant mothers develop gestational diabetes, meaning their cells stop responding properly to the hormone insulin. Breastfeeding has been associated with lower occurrences of Type 2 diabetes in mothers for up to two years after gestational diabetes.[101] The longer a child is breastfed, the lower their chance of that child also developing diabetes later in life.[102] Consuming naturally occurring lactose in breastmilk instead of high fructose corn syrup is much healthier. It primes the body to respond appropriately to appetite cues. It also knows when to shut off the hunger signal, something called satiety, the feeling of being full after a meal. Regular, on-demand access to breastmilk also enhances the "appestat", which we will discuss further in a future chapter. Breastfeeding exclusively up to 12 months old with "baby-led" feeding may promote satiety responsiveness[103].

Obesity – Breastfeeding has a protective effect against childhood obesity[104]. This is because breastfeeding establishes a diverse gut

---

100 van den Elsen, L., Garssen, J., Burcelin, R., & Verhasselt, V. (2019). Shaping the Gut Microbiota by Breastfeeding: The Gateway to Allergy Prevention?. Frontiers in pediatrics, 7, 47. https://doi.org/10.3389/fped.2019.00047

101 Gunderson EP, Hurston SR, Ning X, Lo JC, Crites Y, Walton D, Dewey KG, Azevedo RA, Young S, Fox G, Elmasian CC, Salvador N, Lum M, Sternfeld B, Quesenberry CP Jr; Study of Women, Infant Feeding and Type 2 Diabetes After GDM Pregnancy Investigators. Lactation and Progression to Type 2 Diabetes Mellitus After Gestational Diabetes Mellitus: A Prospective Cohort Study. Ann Intern Med. 2015 Dec 15;163(12):889-98. doi: 10.7326/M15-0807. Epub 2015 Nov 24. PMID: 26595611; PMCID: PMC5193135.

102 Sadauskaite-Kuehne V, Ludvigsson J, Padaiga Z, Jasinskiene E, Samuelsson U. Longer breastfeeding is an independent protective factor against development of type 1 diabetes mellitus in childhood. Diabetes Metab Res Rev. 2004 Mar-Apr;20(2):150-7. doi: 10.1002/dmrr.425. PMID: 15037991.

103 Brown, A., & Lee, M. (2012). Breastfeeding during the first year promotes satiety responsiveness in children aged 18-24 months. Pediatric obesity, 7(5), 382–390. https://doi.org/10.1111/j.2047-6310.2012.00071.x

104 Grube MM, von der Lippe E, Schlaud M, Brettschneider A-K (2015) Does Breastfeeding Help to Reduce the Risk of Childhood Overweight and Obesity? A Propensity Score Analysis of Data from the KiGGS Study. PLoS ONE 10(3): e0122534. doi:10.1371/journal.pone.0122534

flora, cultivating a variety of different species of helpful bacteria. Breastfed babies also have higher leptin in their systems. Leptin is an important appetite regulator chemical. Babies who are exclusively breastfed show self-regulating patterns when they nurse. These are correlated with lower long-term prevention of obesity.[105] Both gut flora and leptin levels play important roles in fat storage. This helps babies form healthy eating patterns. It sets them up for a positive relationship with food as they grow.

NEUROCOGNITIVE DEVELOPMENT

Studies show that babies who are breastfed score higher on intelligence tests. Babies who are fed for a minimum of nine months show improved cognitive development at 1-3 years of age, adjusted to account for other factors like mom's education level and age. The researchers excluded family income level, and adjusted their data to consider the sex, age, and birth weight of the infant. The effect of breastfeeding resulted in a 6.5 to 8.3 jump in IQ points. To put this in perspective, this would move a child from the 39th percentile to the 59th percentile of the population. That change could mean the difference between whether they attend college, their choice of occupation, and the level of social skills.[106]

Much more research should be done in this field. The prevailing theory is that early intake of sufficient amounts of DHA and AA boost brain development, as discussed previously. These important fatty acids contribute to the health of the nervous system. Formula-fed infants have lower DHA levels in their bloodstream. Breastfed humans

---

105   Cannon, A. M., Kakulas, F., Hepworth, A. R., Lai, C. T., Hartmann, P. E., & Geddes, D. T. (2015). The Effects of Leptin on Breastfeeding Behaviour. International journal of environmental research and public health, 12(10), 12340–12355. https://doi.org/10.3390/ijerph121012340

106   Lee, H., Park, H., Ha, E., Hong, Y. C., Ha, M., Park, H., Kim, B. N., Lee, B., Lee, S. J., Lee, K. Y., Kim, J. H., Jeong, K. S., & Kim, Y. (2016). Effect of Breastfeeding Duration on Cognitive Development in Infants: 3-Year Follow-up Study. Journal of Korean medical science, 31(4), 579–584. https://doi.org/10.3346/jkms.2016.31.4.579

and primates also score higher on visual tests too, and these correlate with higher DHA levels as well.[107]

This theory makes sense, given the nutritional difference between breastmilk and formula, particularly in DHA and AA levels. But another important aspect is at play in the development of the nervous system. It may not be totally due to the chemical and nutritional aspect involved. It's the neurology of breastfeeding at its most elegant. It's the total connection and interaction between mother and infant.

For those precious few moments at important intervals throughout the day and night, she may choose to take the opportunity to allow herself to put the phone down, to walk away from other demands and distractions, and simply be a mother in the most supreme and natural sense of the word. The child's active nervous system is calmed and reset as it feeds, relaxes, and recalibrates. Her breathing and heart rate slow and they fall into sync. It is connection and neurological grounding on a fundamental level for both systems. Researchers are beginning to focus on these non-nutritional benefits. They call this concept social-emotional functioning.[108]

Preterm babies are at an inherently higher risk of these things going wrong. Studies repeatedly show one of the greatest predictors of healthy outcomes for these babies is determined by whether they are breastfed or not. One study evaluating brain connectivity found that premature babies that were breastfed more than 75% of their in-patient care had the same brain volume, but had much higher, denser neurological connections in various brain structures.[109] Evidence for this

107   Clandinin, M. T., Jumpsen, J., & Suh, M. (1994). Relationship between fatty acid accretion, membrane composition, and biologic functions. The Journal of pediatrics, 125(5 Pt 2), S25–S32. https://doi.org/10.1016/s0022-3476(06)80733-x

108   Belfort, M. B. (2017). *The science of breastfeeding and brain development | breastfeeding medicine.* Breastfeeding Medicine. Retrieved August 12, 2022, from https://www.liebertpub.com/doi/10.1089/bfm.2017.0122

109   Blesa, M., Sullivan, G., Anblagan, D., Telford, E. J., Quigley, A., Sparrow, S., Serag, A., Semple, S. I., Bastin, M. E., & Boardman, J. P. (n.d.). *Early breast milk exposure modifies brain connectivity in preterm infants.* NeuroImage. Retrieved August 15, 2022, from https://pubmed.ncbi.nlm.nih.gov/30240903/

is based on the largest randomized trial ever conducted on the topic. It studied 17,046 babies who experienced prolonged and exclusive breastfeeding. This group showed higher scores on all intelligence measures, as well as academic ratings in reading and writing.[110]

MATERNAL BENEFITS

Breastfeeding can help mom lose pregnancy weight. It can also help her gain. Feeding may require more calories from her body than when she is not producing breastmilk for her baby. Every mother's genetic and chemical makeup is different. Every woman's body will respond uniquely and marvelously to prolonged breastfeeding. Some women do gain weight during breastfeeding. Others seem to effortlessly lose it. Whatever mother's body and baby's body are responding to, a connected nervous system and the connection of breastfeeding will help it adapt more efficiently.

During feeding, a key hormone is triggered in mother and baby called *oxytocin*. It's associated with infant bonding, loving connections, and belonging. It also plays an important function in aiding with physical healing from the trauma of birth. The smooth muscle of the uterus is very susceptible to the effects of this chemical signal. It aids in slowing blood loss, and in decreasing the size of the uterus, a process called involution. This helps the uterus return to its normal size and location. It prevents problems like uterine prolapse and heavy bleeding after delivery.

The effects of oxytocin on the brain have also been shown to lower the risk of postpartum depression.[111] Discussing this issue is long

110   Kramer, M. S., Aboud, F., Mironova, E., Vanilovich, I., Platt, R. W., Matush, L., Igumnov, S., Fombonne, E., Bogdanovich, N., Ducruet, T., Collet, J. P., Chalmers, B., Hodnett, E., Davidovsky, S., Skugarevsky, O., Trofimovich, O., Kozlova, L., Shapiro, S., & Promotion of Breastfeeding Intervention Trial (PROBIT) Study Group (2008). Breastfeeding and child cognitive development: new evidence from a large, randomized trial. Archives of general psychiatry, 65(5), 578–584. https://doi.org/10.1001/archpsyc.65.5.578
111   Hamdan A, Tamim H. The relationship between postpartum depression and breastfeeding. Int J Psychiatry Med. 2012;43(3):243-59. doi: 10.2190/PM.43.3.d. PMID: 22978082.

overdue. No longer is this downplayed as "baby blues" or dismissed. It is acknowledged as a major part of mom's mental recovery following the delivery. Resources are offered to help treat this complex constellation of symptoms.

Nature offers an array of natural hormones and signal molecules to maintain the delicate chemistry of a healthy nervous system. Sometimes vitamin deficiencies, diet choices, or other contributing factors worsen underlying hormonal issues. These can contribute to postpartum depression. Other times, the body produces enough, but these aren't fully released, or there's something blocking their use. They don't take their marvelous effect on the mind and the healing womb because baby is fed by a bottle, or mom's body is still purging chemical toxins. Baby's love chemical bonds with a rubber nipple or a plastic bag in a tube instead of the warmth and heartbeat at the breast of their mother.

Mothers who breastfeed show a dramatically reduced risk of ovarian and breast cancers. These benefits seem to be cumulative, meaning that the longer a mother nurses, the lower her risk becomes. One study found that women who breastfeed multiple children over 31 months total had a 91% lower risk of ever developing ovarian cancer.[112] Other studies also found a reduced incidence of high blood pressure, arthritis, high blood fats, heart disease, Type 2 diabetes. Breastfeeding may also prevent menstruation, to ensure there is adequate time between pregnancies for mom to recover. Before modern birth control was available, this was nature's way. As an alternative to synthetic hormonal birth control, this is still nature's way of ensuring there are enough resources in the family to go around.

---

112   Dada Su, Maria Pasalich, Andy H Lee, Colin W Binns, Ovarian cancer risk is reduced by prolonged lactation: a case-control study in southern China, The American Journal of Clinical Nutrition, Volume 97, Issue 2, February 2013, Pages 354–359, https://doi.org/10.3945/ajcn.112.044719

These few nutritional and immunological benefits discussed are just the outlines of a much more detailed picture of maternal and infant health. It is around these issues that the most common messages of fear and inadequacy are based that so many mothers are bombarded with daily. The evidence of these powerful advantages should bolster our confidence in the miracle of birth and the power of breastfeeding. Formula simply can't replace this. Breastmilk is unmatched as a nourishing and fortifying tissue, but its biologically intended method of delivery has neurological benefits far beyond the substance itself. Its production threatens formula companies and pharmacies alike. How will they sell you antibiotics for recurring ear infections if breastfed infants suffer them far less often? Where will you spend $1500 a month if you don't give it to them for formula and bottles?

The breastmilk supply is under attack. It faces environmental threats constantly. The effects are very real, regardless of the motivations and money behind it. Massive forces are working on a molecular level to shut down the biological production of the mother's milk supply. In the next chapter, we will learn about the major environmental toxins working against us, and ways we can reduce their impact.

FIVE:
THE HORMONE SYMPHONY: LIVING IN A TOXIC WORLD

THE ENDOCRINE SYSTEM: A CHEMICAL SYMPHONY

The human body utilizes a complex system of chemicals to signal important changes. This messenger system is the *endocrine system*. It is a system of glands, chemical signaling hormones, and receptors that live on the surface of organs and cells to coordinate the behavior of the body, in conjunction with the nervous system's constant connection with every single cell. It is a delicately balanced and very effective chemical pathway. Its hormones act on receptors of special classes of cells to achieve a physical change. This is crucial during preconception, throughout pregnancy, and during delivery. It is critical for a developing baby, for the formation of body structures, both around birth and as children enter puberty. If the right chemicals are produced at the right time, the body knows it produced a viable human that will require milk, and it can signal supply to begin and sustain supply. It's an entire symphony of biochemical changes that prepare for delivery and lactation. Instead of a complicated explanation, let's look at how this system operates generally.

From the moment a mother is pregnant, this system of chemical messengers activates. The elegant signaling alerts the uterus to establish an environment for baby to grow. It also activates the mechanism whereby mother will be able to nurse for the first year of life. It helps form a new digestive system and after delivery, prime it for effective digestion.

Attending an orchestral concert or a symphony event is regretfully becoming more of a rarity these days. Picture the glint of the stage lights off the brass and varnished wood of a huge orchestra, ready to perform an intricate and brilliantly composed masterpiece from one of the ancient, great composers. The conductor will enter the stage to thunderous applause from an excited audience and take their place at the center of the orchestra, on a stand. The concert hall is silent, heavy with the anticipation of the performance. However, the first sound heard from this magnificent system often isn't the opening chords of Beethoven or Rachmaninov. It is a 440 Hz buzz from a single violin, a "Concert Pitch" as it is often called. Almost simultaneously, other violins tune in, as the sound cascades through the violas, cellos and basses. It sounds like an exhilarating hive of bees, all perfectly tuned to the same frequency, and as suddenly as it began, it falls back to an expectant silence. Every eye is on the conductor's stand, the raised baton. Every breath is baited for whatever the opening notes will be.

The central nervous system, the brain and spinal cord, is like that orchestra conductor. Its job is to coordinate the timing and tone of every cell in our body through nerves. Imagine it tapping its baton on the stand, every cell and gland bringing its instrument to attention, primed to perform.

An important structure, called the hypothalamus, is in the center of the brain. This is like the first chair violin, the one charged with tuning the entire symphony. It has been dubbed the "master gland" in the body because it directs so many others. It prepares the orchestra with Concert Pitch, getting every other gland and pathway into perfect frequency and coordination. Another important assistant, called the thalamus, initiates important tasks with chemical signals. These act directly on the body in complex and recently discovered pathways. Sometimes these messages are carried directly to a certain type of tissue to perform a function. Other times they act on yet another gland to release the specific messengers it controls to perform yet a more remote and equally important job. And so on, the chemical cascade goes.

This all happens quickly and constantly. So often we are completely unaware of the intricate dance and balance this system coordinates. We notice it when adrenaline courses through our veins. Or when a ghrelin release signals us that we're hungry for something delicious we see in a commercial. Take the well-known signal chemical insulin. After we consume food, our system turns it into simple sugars which enter the bloodstream. The pancreas releases insulin like a dinner bell. This tells cells to move the sugar inside their walls and turn it into energy.

Diabetes occurs when the body is numb or deaf to the signal of insulin. It no longer responds appropriately to this chemical signal. As a consequence, large quantities of sugar stay in the bloodstream. The cells are where the sugar can be harnessed for energy. When the body fails to manage blood sugar levels, it can negatively impact thyroid and sex hormones[113].

A silent epidemic has been building for decades. It's actually not of diabetes. It's a host of other endocrine disruptions like the example just shared. Our bodies are under siege from chemicals that disrupt

113   Choi, Y. M., Kim, M. K., Kwak, M. K., Kim, D., & Hong, E. G. (2021). Association between thyroid hormones and insulin resistance indices based on the Korean National Health and Nutrition Examination Survey. Scientific reports, 11(1), 21738. https://doi.org/10.1038/s41598-021-01101-z

these signal pathways. Our nervous system is increasingly frustrated. Imagine the conductor furiously pounding the music score, desperately trying to direct this system to produce milk for feeding a hungry baby. But the symphony is chaotic. Different scores are in front of the wrong musicians. Instruments are seated in the wrong sections. Some musicians are walking on stage without their instruments altogether. Some have the wrong instruments. The longer the nervous system's orders go unheeded, the more stressed this system becomes. Imagine the noise coming from such a symphony. Nobody would buy a ticket to hear that sort of noise.

This is so often the pattern of a system in disarray. Women experience migraine headaches, irregular or heavy periods, thyroid conditions, and weight fluctuations. Men have high blood pressure, chronic fatigue, low testosterone, and erectile dysfunction. These are all warning signs that the symphony is not in sync. Instead of a balanced waterfall of chemical signals, from the top down, parts of this cascade are dammed up, water is diverted into other streams and dripping over rocks instead of rushing down freely.

The nervous system tries to speak to a system that is so depleted and disorganized. It loses the ability to mobilize chemicals needed for the desired reactions. No "feedback loop" reaches the central nervous system. The returning signal, like a final confirmation, never reaches the brain. The body doesn't know if the job was completed. It pumps out more chemicals, hoping to hear back. It finally exhausts its supply and gives up.

This is particularly apparent when the body is preparing for breastfeeding. It is so heavily reliant on these chemical signals to prepare the supply. Research is still discovering new pathways of these signal chemicals and hormones in the body. Science is also discovering new sources of interruption, confusion, and dilution.

Scientists observe new ways that toxins make them less effective and chemically, chronically disconnecting human bodies.

These toxins disrupt the natural processes of the body in many ways. This discussion will focus on a specific class of toxins. These are Endocrine Disrupting Chemicals, or EDCs. They are natural and synthetic compounds that affect the delicate delivery system. They are increasingly prevalent in the products in modern use and the environment in which we live. And they are wreaking more havoc on moms and babies than ever before.

CHOOSING TO REDUCE ENVIRONMENTAL TOXINS

Fortunately, the solution to a toxin is straightforward. First eliminate contact, remove it from the system, and then support the body's incredible ability to heal and recover from its effects. A fair warning, however. These EDCs are everywhere. They exist in greater quantities now than ever before. Some of the actions needed to minimize them seem like odd behaviors. There is a good chance of being labeled as a "conspiracy theorist" or a "health nut" if anyone reduces contact with EDCs. It must be recognized as the last-ditch attempt of a desperate system to keep modern families as lifelong consumers and pharmaceutical customers to treat the effects of these toxins. It is an attempt at gaslighting and ostracizing those who would follow suit. Without this chemical noise in the background, the body is running a well-coordinated campaign to produce a steady supply of milk. The rest of the world supply can be shut down or sporadic. Any mother choosing to breastfeed will grateful she took the effort to internalize and implement this information.

This isn't merely having a slightly chubbier baby or being the "crunchy" mom in the soccer or homeschool group. It could, in some instances, mean the difference between life or death. It's certainly the difference between a life of independent health and one of battling opportunistic infections and chronic health concerns. Sometimes however, despite all intentions and the best efforts, milk production fails. It's discouraging, but it's reality. Mothers need space to accept and grieve this, process that disappointment, and know that they did their best. Parents can clean up the endocrine system and follow healthy recommendations to the letter, but in the end, every individual's chemistry is unique.

This is not always a failure. The system may be working perfectly to protect that baby by shutting it down. In a toxic environment, this is actually a favorable, if undesired outcome. Since mother's body relies on chemical signals to coordinate her response, so does a newborn's. There is much less body, so smaller doses of toxins have a larger effect. New structures and developing tissues are very sensitive to toxic disruption. Many hormones are stored in or derived from fat. Newborns are covered with "baby fat", called brown fat. This makes them especially susceptible to absorbing, storing, and later releasing these chemical disruptors. Their body is also newly experiencing these signal molecules outside of the womb. This makes it especially sensitive to anything that blocks or confuses their brand-new receptors.

Mother Nature in her incredible wisdom installed fail-safe systems to protect tiny bodies from a toxic supply. The first line of defense is something called the blood-breast barrier. Not everything in mother's bloodstream has open access to the breast tissue where milk forms. Imagine if our infant formula manufacturers had security guards outside the factory. They wouldn't allow roof repairmen walk on sterile factory floors with dirty boots and non-sanitized hands as Abbott may have[114]. Likewise, mother's body operates the same way in protecting these crucial tissues from toxins and chemicals. Her immune system

---

114   Food and Drug Administration, & Hathaway, T. J., Form FDA 4831-9 (n.d.). Inspectional Observations.

works to keep pathogens and viral particles out. This is why the risk of infecting a newborn with COVID-19 via breastmilk is so miniscule, and why breastfeeding has always been safe and internationally recommended[115] outside the United States.

The backup system, for a mother who is so flooded with toxins, is an increasingly common route today. The body simply shuts down the supply of milk. From an evolutionary perspective, this is a huge benefit to the species. If a particular mother is incapable of producing a healthy, pure supply for a growing baby, perhaps another method is needed to feed this baby. Nature's innate intelligence will not allow corrupt milk to be passed along to the newborn. It's the natural version of the FDA quality inspectors, except that these actually do their job.

Certain medications and antibiotics are capable of crossing the blood-breast barrier and can diffuse into the milk supply. In sufficient quantities, they could change the natural production of breastmilk. They affect the delicate mammary gland cells. Supply halts. It may be surprising what common EDCs can slip into the factory undetected. Once this is realized, it's easier to recognize why so many mothers are "losing their supply", or just can't seem to "produce enough milk". Instead of choosing to view it as failing to provide milk for a baby, it can be reframed as succeeding in stopping a toxic cascade. It is halting the transmission from the environment to babies. In that regard, viewed in that light, shutting down supply is the healthiest, smartest, safest thing a mother's body can do. Such a response can make it easier to accept and honor that decision.

---

115   Pereira, A., Cruz-Melguizo, S., Adrien, M. et al. Breastfeeding mothers with COVID-19 infection: a case series. Int Breastfeed J 15, 69 (2020). https://doi.org/10.1186/s13006-020-00314-8

THE FIRST LINE OF DEFENSE

How much better would it be to reduce or eliminate toxins in the first place? Preparation for breastfeeding can begin with all the other prenatal work mother may be doing. She can confidently rely on the first line of defense against chemicals and bacteria. As a backup, she can trust the blood-breast barrier after addressing the environment. Otherwise, she risks her body pressing the big red shutoff switch on the whole operation to protect her baby. Let's be grateful that emergency measure exists. It's far better than the alternative of polluting the food supply of breastfeeding newborns.

During the month before delivery, the umbilical cord transports at least 300 quarts of blood daily back and forth across the womb. One study tested this blood for industrial pollutants in a group of ten babies. They found 287 chemicals present. 180 of which cause cancer, 217 of which are toxic to the brain and nervous system, and 208 which are known to cause birth defects.[116] Only in recent decades has the technology existed to detect such tiny amounts of toxins, but what this is telling us about our environment is important.

We are birthing babies who have been industrially polluted. We must address this "body burden" as early and as often as possible. It can be incredibly overwhelming as you become aware of these environmental toxins. As stated, EDCs are everywhere. Trust your instincts and realize you can eliminate these slowly over time. Your body will help you, as you ease the toxic burden. Small changes today can have huge impacts later in life. Some principles to consider as you decide which ones to tackle first:

---

116 *Body burden: The pollution in newborns.* Environmental Working Group. (2005, July 14). Retrieved August 15, 2022, from https://www.ewg.org/research/body-burden-pollution-newborns

1. *Frequency of contact*: How often is this product in use? How long has contact with that toxin occurred? Focus on things used every day, or multiple times a day. Consider reducing the number exposures. Is it used once briefly? Or does it stay on the body or clothing for the whole day? Focus also on frequency. Things like deodorant, toothpaste, cosmetics, detergents, and hair products are big ones. These are in constant, intimate contact with the largest, most porous organ, the skin. Skin is constantly absorbing low doses of the toxins throughout the day, and likely has been doing it for as long as the brand has been in use.

2. *Dosage matters*. How much of the toxin is in the environment is important. If it can't be eliminated completely, look for ways at lowering the amount of it the body has to deal with. Can hand sanitizer be traded for soap and water? Can you use less of a particular perfume or air freshener?

3. *Timing is important*. Bodies respond differently throughout the day or even over the course of our lives. A mother and father attempting to conceive should review their environment carefully and supportively. EDCs negatively impact the chances of fertility in both sexes. They can affect sperm count, quality, and motility. Newborns are especially susceptible to interference, and pre-adolescent children are also often overlooked. As the body is preparing for pregnancy or puberty, it needs extra focus on what is going on chemically. Any support in eliminating endocrine "noise" from the outside world goes a long way, especially at crucial intervals when a fully functioning orchestra is required to coordinate chemical tasks.

Begin now. Take small steps to unwind the toxic whirlwind in bathrooms, laundry rooms, and kitchens. These little actions are significant. This may mean parting with beloved brands. Brands have marketed to you for years or decades to secure a psychological allegiance to them. Smell is one of the strongest senses associated with our memories. These two things are closely associated neurologically. Smelling your grandfather's favorite cologne brings back a cascade of childhood memories. For an aftershave to be so potent, however, it must contain a cocktail of unstable aromatics and chemicals. These are intended to constantly fall apart and waft into our noses. These bind with the sensitive mucous linings of our sinuses. They can create chronic sinus infections, headaches, and general inflammation. Our body has to fight to detoxify these areas. It is already fighting to keep germs away from them. Inflammation and chemicals only complicate this mission.

Sadly, the products that smell the nicest and most familiar tend to be those that make us the sickest. It's a tough habit to break. Social feeds have learned consumer behaviors, and preys on loyalty to these products. It will encourage customers to order them again. It will show bulk discounts and sweeten the deal. This is the cost of breaking free from the grasp of this huge marketing machine. Waking up is worth it. Be ready to embrace change.

BABY STEPS

Start now to create a healthy environment. There will be awkward and maybe even adversarial conversations. There may be relapses where the temptation to go back to previous products is too strong. But this isn't failure. Read the labels again. Think of what these EDCs are costing, now and in the future. It's costing self-sufficiency. It might cost baby's access to a healthy breastmilk supply.

What follows are a few major categories of EDCs, where they are found, and what is important to know about each. These are not listed in any order in terms of most toxic or common. This list is not a complete inventory, but it's some of the main ones that concern breastmilk supply, based on what research is available. Each person has a unique chemical makeup and a highly personalized cabinet of poisons. Each has their own journey to eliminate these. Eventually a threshold is met where the body resumes normal operations. It begins to signal again as it can clear the system and process these toxins out. This relies on kidney and liver function, some sweat, and a lot of patience and consistency. There are some things we can do to support those efforts, and we will discuss them next.

Women use products every day that are in prolonged contact with their skin. Anything that goes onto the surface of the skin can end up in the bloodstream. This is a key delivery system for EDCs. Certain aspects of EDCs affect minority individuals disproportionately. Some product lines and straighteners in ethnic-specific markets affect black American consumers more. These products have been cited as a possible contributing factor for some of the racial disparity noted with preterm deliveries as well.[117] Black mothers struggle most, compared to Hispanic and white mothers, in exclusively breastfeeding to six months. There is increasing evidence this could be due to greater contact with disrupting chemicals leading to low breastmilk supply.

For example, keratin straightening treatments used by black Americans contain formaldehyde, which is a potent allergen and a known cause of cancer. It's highly concentrated in hair straighteners. These products may also contain lead acetate, a neurotoxin. While the long-term effects of daily use have not been clearly established,

117   Preston, E. V., Fruh, V., Quinn, M. R., Hacker, M. R., Wylie, B. J., O'Brien, K., Mahalingaiah, S., & James-Todd, T. (2021). Endocrine disrupting chemical-associated hair product use during pregnancy and gestational age at delivery: a pilot study. Environmental health : a global access science source, 20(1), 86. https://doi.org/10.1186/s12940-021-00772-5

constant contact with these types of chemicals would be a logical explanation for the frustration we see in Black mothers who choose to breastfeed, based on the numbers they report. We need more data. And we need it to come from studies conducted by someone other than the manufacturers of the products being sold.

Rather than an exhaustive treatise on each of these elements, these are included as a general overview here. It's easy to feel overwhelmed and powerless to change. Refuse to accept this normal. Join a community of like-minded parents, a farm co-op, a naturally minded mom group, or the Starving Babies community. If you are looking for an action plan, a step-by-step elimination plan is available at starvingbabies.com. More detailed descriptions and relevant research is included there so we don't get bogged down here. Note the long chemical names that effectively keep these chemicals out of normal conversation, followed by the alphabet soup shorthand to make it easier to discuss:

PHTHALATES (Pronounced "THAY-lates")

These are scent binders that are most-often found in nail polish, hairspray, and fragrant products. Scented candles and aromatic wax melts, car air fresheners, and other scented products contain these. They are common in plastic food storage containers too and help reduce or contain odors. They coat many children's toys and are in any plastic wrap derived from PVC. Plastic that contains phthalates will often have a "#3" within the recycling symbol. Higher levels of phthalates in the urine of pregnant women have been related with long-term changes in maternal weight[118] and an increased risk of preterm birth[119].

---

118   Rodríguez-Carmona, Y., Cantoral, A., Trejo-Valdivia, B., Téllez-Rojo, M. M., Svensson, K., Peterson, K. E., Meeker, J. D., Schnaas, L., Solano, M., & Watkins, D. J. (2019). Phthalate exposure during pregnancy and long-term weight gain in women. Environmental research, 169, 26–32. https://doi.org/10.1016/j.envres.2018.10.014

119   U.S. Department of Health and Human Services. (2022, July 11). Preterm birth more likely with

FRAGRANCE/PARFUM

Unfortunately, fragrances are not limited just to perfumes and body sprays. Deodorants, shampoos, and more contain "fragrance" which is also often labeled as "parfum". Under the labeling and ingredient laws, manufacturers don't have to disclose the contents of these "fragrances". This allows them to keep their recipes secret. A 2010 report found an average of 14 different types of EDC chemicals not listed on product labels, but under the term "fragrance". Only 34% of these ingredients have any published safety assessments.[120] Strong smells indicate very unstable molecules. When working to detoxify and clear out your endocrine system, get comfortable with no smells or chemical odors. You may notice improvements in "seasonal allergy" symptoms, easier breathing or fewer asthma attacks. Sinus and breathing problems improve, and your nose becomes more sensitized to the subtler, natural odors. Keep in mind too that baby's nose is finely tuned to your natural smell, and strong-smelling chemicals and heavily scented lotions can lower their interest in latching, and can cause eczema and rashes in both mother and baby, due to the constantly changing hormone and inflammation levels.

TRICLOSANS (TCS)

This is a strongly acknowledged disruptor and has been banned in most countries. In the United States it is allowed in toothpaste, hand sanitizer, and mouthwash. It's common in products that touch the thin, sensitive membranes covering the mucosa, like inside the mouth where the skin is thinnest. This makes it highly absorbable. Consider how often people are pumping hand sanitizer onto their skin on a daily and hourly basis. Skip the Purel pump. Find a natural hand sanitizer

exposure to phthalates. National Institutes of Health. Retrieved August 22, 2022, from https://www.nih.gov/news-events/news-releases/preterm-birth-more-likely-exposure-phthalates

120   Sarantis, H., Naidenko, O. V., Gray, S., Houlihan, J., & Malkan, S. (2010, May 12). *Not so Sexy - Environmental Working Group.* The Health Risks of Secret Chemicals in Fragrance. Retrieved August 16, 2022, from https://www.ewg.org/sites/default/files/report/SafeCosmetics_FragranceRpt.pdf

or wash your hands with conventional water and soap (triclosan free hand soap, that is.) Mothers with detectable levels of triclosans in their milk supply had babies with less bacterial diversity in their gut,[121] weakening the immune system and digestive tract.

UV FILTERS

Two major chemicals that cause absolute chaos in our bodies, are oxybenzone and benzophenone. These chemicals alter natural gene expression. They turn off certain proteins and turn on others. They also impair fertility by interfering with sperm function.[122] This has terrifying implications for moms who are trying to express genes naturally. These chemicals easily breach the blood-breast barrier and accumulate in breast tissue. They are lipophilic, meaning they get absorbed in the fat deposits that should be feeding baby clean breastmilk. These are found in sunscreen products and lotions, as well as nail polish and lip balm. Nail polish may not seem like a big deal, but our nail beds and cuticles are highly absorbant areas. These chemicals keep colors from fading. They even make us feel protected from sunburn. They're marketed as a way to reduce skin cancer, but the evidence is controversial and is still evolving. As with previous chemicals, more studies are needed by unbiased scientists. UV Filtering chemicals have no business infiltrating breastmilk supply.

BISPHENOL A (BPAs)

This includes two more classes of chemicals, in addition to BPA, which are BPF and BPS. Companies often advertise something as "BPA Free". Sometimes this is replaced with one of the far worse cousins, BPF/

121   Bever, C. S., Rand, A. A., Nording, M., Taft, D., Kalanetra, K. M., Mills, D. A., Breck, M. A., Smilowitz, J. T., German, J. B., & Hammock, B. D. (2018). Effects of triclosan in breast milk on the infant fecal microbiome. Chemosphere, 203, 467–473. https://doi.org/10.1016/j.chemosphere.2018.03.186

122   Rehfeld, A., Egeberg, D. L., Almstrup, K., Petersen, J. H., Dissing, S., & Skakkebæk, N. E. (2018). EDC IMPACT: Chemical UV filters can affect human sperm function in a progesterone-like manner. Endocrine connections, 7(1), 16–25. https://doi.org/10.1530/EC-17-0156

BPS. Unfortunately, labeling is often more a part of marketing than it is for safety or quality of the contents. A recent study found that 93% of Americans contain measurable levels of this toxin in their blood and tissues.[123] This poison alters the genes that are responsible for uterine development and fertility.[124] It is found in the interior lining of canned foods. This is a reason to avoid or decrease canned food consumption. Its highest dosages are found in the paper of store receipts used in thermal printers like at big box stores. These change the white paper to black. From receipts it is easily transferred to our fingertips or the lining of our pockets and quickly absorbed into the bloodstream. Imagine the frequency of shoppers who pump triclosans onto their hands with hand sanitizers as they reach for a BPA laden receipt with the other. Another common culprit is in the lids of coffee cups.[125] It is easily activated and freed by heat when you sip your favorite warm beverage through that tiny opening in the plastic loaded with BPA, which can mimic estrogen and confuse the orchestra. Any plastic that has a "PC" (polycarbonate) label, or a "#7" in the symbol is a carrier for BPA.

POLYFLUOROALKYL SUBSTANCES (PFAs)

These are most common in non-stick surfaces of cookware, like Teflon™. Tiny chips or scrapes of these surfaces transfer it into the food and into the bloodstream. The body has a hard time eliminating it. Waterproof coating and water-resistant surfaces also contain these endocrine disruptors. These chemicals, like the PBDEs, have been shown to be doubling every four years, accumulating in breast tissue

123   U.S. Department of Health and Human Services. (2021, November). *Bisphenol A (BPA)*. National Institute of Environmental Health Sciences. Retrieved August 15, 2022, from https://www.niehs.nih.gov/health/topics/agents/sya-bpa/index.cfm

124   The Endocrine Society. (2009, June 12). Bisphenol A Exposure In Pregnant Mice Permanently Changes DNA Of Offspring. ScienceDaily. Retrieved August 14, 2022 from www.sciencedaily.com/releases/2009/06/090610124428.htm

125   Bittner, G.D., Denison, M.S., Yang, C.Z. et al. Chemicals having estrogenic activity can be released from some bisphenol a-free, hard and clear, thermoplastic resins. Environ Health 13, 103 (2014). https://doi.org/10.1186/1476-069X-13-103

and currently found in 100% of tested women[126]. In 1999, Switzerland began to examine levels of PFAs in breastmilk. They discovered that mothers exposed to this toxin in their drinking water had an increased risk of not initiating breastfeeding or having shorter breastfeeding duration.[127] These chemicals are linked to weakened immune systems, thyroid disorders, and metabolism issues.[128] Companies have been switching to "newer" versions of this toxin, but it's clear that the cumulative effect of these and their prevalence in breastmilk is threatening the health and integrity of the breastmilk supply.

POLYBROMINATED DIPHENYL ETHERS/BIPHENYLS (PBDEs/PBBs)

This class of chemical is used in fire retardants. They have also been introduced into most flame-retardant household items and furniture. These molecules often hitchhike in that multicolored carpet padding, or in furniture upholstery. It is best to avoid recently upholstered furniture or newly installed carpet to reduce contact with PBDEs. Another option is to choose a home with tile or wood floors and use throw rugs. If this is not feasible, ensure adequate time to "off-gas". Using a vacuum with a HEPA filter will help trap these troublesome molecules before they begin to circulate in the air. A HEPA rated air filter can help trap them once they are. Furniture and carpet can be flame resistant, but breast tissue shouldn't be.

126   Zheng, G., Schreder, E., Dempsey, J. C., Uding, N., Chu, V., Andres, G., Sathyanarayana, S., & Salamova, A. (2021, April 25). *Per- and Polyfluoroalkyl Substances (PFAS) in Breast Milk: Concerning Trends for Current-Use PFAS*. Cen.acs.org. Retrieved August 18, 2022, from https://cen.acs.org/environment/persistent-pollutants/PFAS-pervade-breast-milk/99/i19

127   Nielsen, C., Li, Y., Lewandowski, M., Fletcher, T., & Jakobsson, K. (2022). Breastfeeding initiation and duration after high exposure to perfluoroalkyl substances through contaminated drinking water: A cohort study from Ronneby, Sweden. Environmental research, 207, 112206. https://doi.org/10.1016/j.envres.2021.112206

128   Guomao Zheng, Erika Schreder, Jennifer C. Dempsey, Nancy Uding, Valerie Chu, Gabriel Andres, Sheela Sathyanarayana, and Amina Salamova Environmental Science & Technology 2021 55 (11), 7510-7520 DOI: 10.1021/acs.est.0c06978

GLYPHOSATE

This is a common one, and is part of a much bigger, urgent national conversation. It is the chemical mentioned in the beginning of the book. Glyphosate is most famously found in Round-Up®, the controversial weed killer that sits in most garages. It's also sprayed onto most yards. It runs into most gutters during rainstorms or yard and garden waterings and ends up in most ground water. Traces of this remain on produce, and tiny traces are ingested in foods tainted with residues of this powerful organic toxin.

If you recall, in 2011 the government was concerned some of the soy-based baby formulas could be tainted with this known poison. They tested nearly 300 samples of the top brands. 271 of those tested came back positive for glyphosate.[129] Did the government take action to address the contaminated food chain? Did they set standards for cleanliness and toxin-free products in soy formula makers? Did the manufacturer Monsanto address this problem and own up to it? None of the above. The government decided to no longer test for glyphosate residue in infant formulas for unstated reasons. Glyphosate is a known neurotoxin at a time when mothers are growing a brand-new nervous system and a brain. It also destroys gut bacteria and the delicate balance of cultures we work so hard to establish.

DIOXINS

Dioxins form whenever chlorine or bromine burns in the presence of oxygen or carbon. It can happen near garbage dump sites with incinerators, industrial plants, and similar places. Think of it as tiny, toxic pieces of ash that accumulate in our food chain. It is present in

129   Gillam, C. (2015, April 17). *U.S. regulators may recommend testing food for glyphosate residues.* Reuters. Retrieved August 10, 2022, from https://www.reuters.com/article/us-food-agriculture-glyphosate/u-s-regulators-may-recommend-testing-food-for-glyphosate-residues-idUSKBN0N82K020150417

most of our store-bought meats, fish, milk, butter, and eggs. Whenever we use chlorine to control bacterial growth in food, once it is cooked and the chlorine burns, dioxins infiltrate our foods. Switching to farm grown or farm-to-table food supply may help reduce the intake of dioxins. Dioxin exposure has been observed to shut down 50% of new mammary cells in breast tissue. It alters the expression of breastmilk-producing genes, by slowing down the number of branches and lobules in mammary tissue. This damage was so extensive in the lab studies that rats were unable to nurse their babies.[130] Dioxins are almost everywhere nowadays. Being aware of our food supply is a helpful start at cleaning them up. This toxin is especially important to address before the beginning of pregnancy since breast tissue begins to initiate changes within nine days of conception and implantation.

PERCHLORATES

Perchlorates are rocket fuel. That is not a metaphor; it's actually rocket fuel. It is found in trace amounts in most of our produce and milk. It's especially pernicious, because it binds with thyroid tissue and competes with iodine for normal thyroid function. We also increase our exposure to it when we wash our fruits and vegetables in bleach. The FDA recently decided to allow food companies to use perchlorate as an anti-static agent in plastic packaging for food[131], despite established research that shows the damage this type of toxin inflicts on the endocrine system. Monitoring iodine intake and using a water filter rated for perchlorates are great places to start in reducing exposure.

---

130   Vorderstrasse, B. A., Fenton, S. E., Bohn, A. A., Cundiff, J. A., & Lawrence, B. P. (2004). A novel effect of dioxin: exposure during pregnancy severely impairs mammary gland differentiation. Toxicological sciences : an official journal of the Society of Toxicology, 78(2), 248–257. https://doi.org/10.1093/toxsci/kfh062

131   Food and Drug Administration. (2022, April 13). *Threshold of regulation (TOR) exemptions.* Threshold of Regulation (TOR) Exemptions. Retrieved August 22, 2022, from https://www.cfsanappsexternal.fda.gov/scripts/fdcc/index.cfm?set=TOR&id=2005-006&sort=File&order=DESC&startrow=1&type=basic&search=perchlorate

LEAD

Lead serves no useful biological purpose in the body. It's usually taken orally, through contaminated water or food. It circulates in the blood for about thirty days and is slowly absorbed into soft tissues and bone. Once there, it may stay up to 27 years. From newborn to age six, the damage of lead in the system is especially noticeable since the nervous system is developing during this time. Since lead can be stored in bone, as mom's body utilizes calcium from her bones during pregnancy and breastfeeding, some of this previously stored lead can be released into her bloodstream and can pass to baby. This significantly alters IQ and neurobehavior in kids.[132] Unfortunately, we still find trace amounts of lead in old paint, in groundwater, and other sources. This is another reason that investing in a quality water filtration system for your home is an excellent idea. If lead levels are especially high, the process known as chelation may help draw heavy metals from bone and tissues. This is something that should be checked and undertaken with a medical expert well before baby is on-board and not while breastfeeding. Lead levels in the blood will be high while the body processes this out.

ARSENIC

Arsenic acts on the *glucocorticoid regulated system*. This means in small doses it changes how our the metabolizes and uses energy from our food. It can lead to weight gain and loss, protein wasting disease, and can severely damage the immune system. It makes us less sensitive to insulin, causes bone density to decrease, delays growth, and causes high blood pressure. Like lead, this is often found in groundwater and can be filtered out with an at-home filtration system.

---

132   *Breastfeeding and Lead Contamination.* InfantRisk Center. (2016, March 10). Retrieved August 23, 2022, from https://www.infantrisk.com/breastfeeding-and-lead-contamination

MERCURY

Many mothers have endured lectures on avoiding the effects of mercury on the developing fetus and our nervous systems. They are told to avoid sushi during pregnancy. Mercury is a known neurotoxin that may be lurking in old dental work and seafood. Mercury comes in inorganic and organic forms. The organic forms include methyl mercury, which is commonly found in seafood, and ethyl mercury, also called thimerosal. Since there seems to be a direct relationship with the levels of mercury mother and baby are exposed to, and the incidence of neurological problems, there is no safe dose based on literature for mercury exposure. American health experts assure us that the amounts of mercury in certain products they recommend for injection is so low that they should not concern us. A growing body of research, however, is not so sure. One study, for example, in the International Journal of Environmental Research and Public Health, found evidence supporting a significant relationship between exposure to thimerosal [mercury] and the subsequent risk of neurodevelopmental diagnosis.[133] It is up to parents to check the labels of anything intended for injection into either mother's or baby's body. Mercury may also be found in some cosmetics, where it is used to slow bacteria and fungal growth. Choosing wild-caught salmon or farm-fed trout is a good way to reduce mercury consumption. Avoiding large, predatory species like swordfish and albacore tuna, which tend to accumulate organic mercury in their tissues as they age, is also a good choice.

GLYCOL ETHERS

These are another very common type of EDCs found in paints, cleaning supplies, brake fluid, and many cosmetics. During the "nesting phase"

---

133   Geier, D. A., Hooker, B. S., Kern, J. K., King, P. G., Sykes, L. K., & Geier, M. R. (2014). A dose-response relationship between organic mercury exposure from thimerosal-containing vaccines and neurodevelopmental disorders. International journal of environmental research and public health, 11(9), 9156–9170. https://doi.org/10.3390/ijerph110909156

of pregnancy, many moms and dads will paint the nursery, which exposes them to these fumes. Traces of these chemicals were found in over 90% of pregnant mothers tested and were associated with developmental problems in their children at six years of age.[134] Even with a long off-gassing period, allowing the fumes to dissipate, it is possible for babies and children to inhale glycol ethers from the paint for years to come. This often may present as asthma since the body's intelligence attempts to slow the inhalation of these toxins. Airways may be intuitively constricting to reduce the intake of the harmful fumes. These glycol ethers are also associated with allergies. The mucous linings are trying to congest and block the invasion of these particles into the upper respiratory system. Be mindful of what paint products are used, and when they are deployed.

Our programmed reaction to such a list is a sense of panic or paranoia. This is because so much of our media works to convince the majority of the population that everything is deadly. These same mouthpieces simultaneously advertise products that are riddled with toxins. The result is pushing more drugs and medications for side-effects and increasing your reliance on Big Pharma and the medical infrastructure. This is a frustrating reality. When government agencies exist for the expressed purpose of protecting the consumers, why are mothers and babies increasingly bearing the body burden of chronic toxin exposure? Who does the government really represent? Are tax dollars paying more than lobby dollars? Their loyalty at the end of the day is to the highest bidder. Every family must choose for themselves who to trust. But consumers vote with their dollars. They can stop funding them. Customers don't need Congress to do it, they can begin a grassroots boycott of the bad actors and toxic producers.

---

134   Béranger, R., Garlantézec, R., Le Maner-Idrissi, G., Lacroix, A., Rouget, F., Trowbridge, J., Warembourg, C., Monfort, C., Le Gléau, F., Jourdin, M., Multigner, L., Cordier, S., & Chevrier, C. (2017). Prenatal Exposure to Glycol Ethers and Neurocognitive Abilities in 6-Year-Old Children: The PELAGIE Cohort Study. Environmental health perspectives, 125(4), 684–690. https://doi.org/10.1289/EHP39

Rather than racing to panic about this, focus on the fact that the human body is incredibly adept at containing, breaking down, and expelling toxins. The filtering organs simply wear out from doing that at such high levels for so long. Especially as mothers prepare for pregnancy and breastfeeding, their bodies need to focus their energy on building a baby. They have a complex task to perform, and we need to support them wherever we can. Any little help will yield huge returns, because toxin-free, low stress living is what they are designed to do. Resiliency, recovery, repair, and restoration are the watchwords. Here are the beginning principles of the way to freedom from environmental stressors. This is how to clean up the endocrine system, prepare for a clean and reliable breastmilk supply, purify baby's bloodstream, and protect our environment from toxins.

ELIMINATION

One simple action plan is to make a list of all the chemical products contacted in the course of a day. Go through cabinets and showers and write down the brands used in the family, and maybe a month or year number on how long such has been the case. Visit starvingbabies. com to find a template to get started, and some research links as information evolves and becomes available.

Then visit ewg.org/skindeep and look up those products. Over 90,000 common products from 3,000 brands have been studied for these EDCs, and this resource will indicate if a certain product holds up to their hype of "natural, clean, organic, safe" and display a rating to gauge roughly how healthy these products are.

Begin eliminating in small steps. Every switch to a better, baby-friendly, breastfeeding supportive product is progress. Don't feel you need to overhaul every cabinet and bathroom cupboard in the house overnight. It's expensive and can be self-defeating. Instead, take logical, consistent measures to reduce your toxic load. Notice the improvements to your body and your energy levels. Celebrate the progress and recognize this is a process. It must be sustainable. Many of these volatile compounds have a short half-life, meaning they break down and exit your body fairly quickly. While the damage they inflict is real, your body can recover. Just focus on supporting it and do your best not to put more in.

Remember too that marketers understand that "clean" sells, and they know how the system works. The FDA is the only regulatory agency in this space, and they claim no authority to regulate chemicals categorized as fragrances in the products they allow to market.[135] The European Union conducts extensive testing and updates their regulations against EDCs in cosmetics often. To date, they have banned over 1,300 chemicals as endocrine disruptors from their cosmetics industry. In comparison, the United States has restricted just eleven.[136] Part of this is due to the EU's practice of preventive and cautionary approaches to chemical disruptors. If it's suspicious, they err on the side of keeping it out of cosmetics. Some of this difference is due to the slow pace that the FDA moves at regulating, Companies pay good money to get their products to market. Their labeling as "non-GMO", "all-natural", and "organic" bear closer scrutiny, because the government can and does allow a broad definition of these terms. It may not always be as it claims.

WATER

Detoxification is a word that is so often thrown around nowadays, it has almost lost its meaning. While certain compounds can help

135 Sarantis, H., Naidenko, O. V., Gray, S., Houlihan, J., & Malkan, S. (2010, May 12). *Not so Sexy - Environmental Working Group*. The Health Risks of Secret Chemicals in Fragrance. Retrieved August 16, 2022, from https://www.ewg.org/sites/default/files/report/SafeCosmetics_FragranceRpt.pdf
136 Milman, O. (2019, May 22). *US cosmetics are full of chemicals banned by Europe – why?* The Guardian. Retrieved August 15, 2022, from https://www.theguardian.com/us-news/2019/may/22/chemicals-in-cosmetics-us-restricted-eu

support the body's detoxification process, we mainly rely on the liver and kidneys to filter out most of the junk in our system. This is why drinking clean water often is so important. It literally flushes the toxin from our system. Bottled water has a potential to be polluted and may be contaminated with microplastics and BPA. If you are drinking water at a restaurant from a plastic cup or with a straw, decline a lemon wedge. The citric acid can leach plastic into your water and increase your exposure. If you're drinking from glassware, lemon water or essential oil is a great way to support your body's filtration system, as it still breaks down the plastic. It is much more helpful when this reaction occurs in the bloodstream, instead of in plastic drinkware or a plastic straw. Protect a clean water supply. It's the cornerstone of healthy detoxification, hydration, and purification. Consider investing in a simple in-line or gravity-fed system at home and commit to servicing the filter regularly. Charcoal is a powerful filter medium for many of the poisonous molecules we just discussed. Recommended filters are available on this book's website.

SUPPLEMENTAL SUPPORT AND SAUNA

You can also investigate consuming things like activated charcoal, food-grade diatomaceous earth, chlorella and spirulina, and certain types of mushrooms to assist in the detoxification process. For heavy metals, there are great benefits to saunas. The sweet spot seems to be in using a sauna between 160- and 200-degrees Fahrenheit, four to seven times a week for about 20 minutes each session.[137] Using a sauna while pregnant is not recommended, as the effects on a developing fetus have not been evaluated. Similarly, avoid hot tubs, since the water never cools and can lead to overheating. A warm bath is fine, since the water cools naturally. If sauna is included in the preconception

137 Mercola, J. (2022, May 8). The Stunning Health Benefits of Sauna Therapy [web log]. Retrieved August 16, 2022.

preparations, however, there is a huge benefit to eliminating heavy metals like cadmium, mercury, lead, arsenic, and more. These elements are found in higher concentration in sweat than in urine.[138] Phthalates and BPA are excreted more effectively through the urine, so be sure to stay well-hydrated and consider adding a pinch of Himalayan rock salt to your water to keep your electrolyte levels in balance. Also consider switching to a simple French press, since household coffee makers often have plastic reservoirs and phthalate-based tubing. Check labels on brands of tea, as many teabags contain BPA.

PRENATAL CHIROPRACTIC

Maintaining a strong and resilient nervous system is also crucial for coordinating the elimination of toxins. The optimization of the central nervous system is the objective of the chiropractic profession. If you have not done so already, interview chiropractors and find one who is aligned with supporting you on your birth journey and is specifically trained to do so. Preconception care for both parents is a great way to begin a successful pregnancy. The benefits extend far beyond the regular hip pain and low back challenges of pregnancy. Remember that the nervous system regulates everything, and chiropractic care optimizes that master system. For example, regular bowel movements with softer stool[139] have been correlated with regular chiropractic care. This is helpful during the detoxification phase preconception, as well as during pregnancy with pregnancy-related constipation.

There is a part of the nervous system that is not under consciously control, which regulates heartrate, digestion, and breathing, all the things that happen automatically. This is called, appropriately, the

---

138   Sears, M. E., Kerr, K. J., & Bray, R. I. (2012). Arsenic, cadmium, lead, and mercury in sweat: a systematic review. *Journal of environmental and public health, 2012*, 184745. https://doi.org/10.1155/2012/184745
139   Redly, M. (2001). *The effects of chiropractic care on a patient with chronic constipation.* Journal of Canadian Chiropractic Association. Retrieved August 16, 2022, from https://www.chiropractic.ca/wp-content/uploads/2014/07/Pages185-191.pdf

"autonomic" nervous system, meaning "self-governing." This system speeds processes up and slows them down as needed. It has two modes: fight or flight, and rest and digest, essentially a gas pedal and a brake. Far too many expectant mothers spend much of their pregnancy in the protective and defensive "fight or flight" mode. Many of them feel stressed and fatigued, both symptoms of too much gas pedal on this part of the nervous system.

A neurologically based chiropractor specifically trained in adjusting pregnant mothers can help with this. The adjustment can take mother's keyed up nervous system back to balance and ease. This will also allow baby's nervous system to learn to hardwire the "rest and digest" mode. The way that mother's system is trained to respond to her environment is how the baby's developing system will learn to cope as well. When mother is at ease, that tiny nervous system will learn to use the brake pads appropriately. This is where the healthiest babies nurse, sleep, poop, and grow, because that system is functioning the way it was designed.

Regular chiropractic care throughout pregnancy has also been associated with 24-39% less labor time[140], and reports of less pain during labor. Published evidence is increasingly showing that regular chiropractic care "may improve the probability of successful natural parturition[141]", or childbirth. It has been found to help with constipation, bloating, and swelling during pregnancy. The American Pregnancy Association approves of chiropractic care during pregnancy.[142] Patients also report improved sleep and digestion overall. One study documented that the production of breastmilk *doubled*

140   Fallon J.M. Chiropractic and pregnancy: a partnership for the future. ICA Int Rev Chiropr. 1990;46(6):39–42.
141   Borggren, C. L. (2007, June 20). *Pregnancy and chiropractic: A narrative review of the literature.* Journal of Chiropractic Medicine. Retrieved August 16, 2022, from https://www.sciencedirect.com/science/article/pii/S0899346707000444
142   Editor. (2022, June 8). *Chiropractic care during pregnancy.* American Pregnancy Association. Retrieved August 16, 2022, from https://americanpregnancy.org/healthy-pregnancy/pregnancy-health-wellness/chiropractic-care-during-pregnancy/

following chiropractic adjusting, and that contributed to successful breastfeeding at ten months postpartum.[143]

This makes total sense with what is currently understood about the neurology of breastfeeding. When the orchestra is in tune, and oxytocin production is occurring naturally and plentifully, it signals the release of milk when baby is hungry. This "let down" or ejection reflex is critical. Sometimes, however, a drop in dopamine, a feel-good hormone, occurs when milk production begins. This can lead to a brief but intense feeling ranging from depression to self-loathing. This problem is called Dysphoric Milk Ejection Reflex, or D-MER. Let your doctor know if this occurs, and oftentimes just being aware of this phenomenon is enough to help.[144] Regulating these important hormones release by supporting the central nervous system is important too. And this is where chiropractic care can truly shine. That nervous system is the conductor for the orchestra, and the chemical symphony responds to the cues it takes from mother's environment.

CONFIDENCE OVER CONCERN

It's easy to get caught up and even obsess over toxins in the environment. Human bodies are incredibly resilient, especially during pregnancy and breastfeeding. They can protect the precious blood and milk supply to baby, and simply becoming aware provides new ways to support this process. Parents can reduce their exposure or intake, and help fight any pollution or damage that may have already occurred. Entire organ systems are dedicated to this effort, and there are multiple ways of supporting them in this role. Pick one that is

---

143   Baumm, A. (2020, March 10). *Resolution of milk ejection reflex dysfunction & increased breastmilk supply following chiropractic adjustment in a nursing mother of twins: A case report & review of the literature.* Vertebral Subluxation Research. Retrieved August 16, 2022, from https://vertebralsubluxationresearch.com/2020/02/27/resolution-of-milk-ejection-reflex-dysfunction-increased-breastmilk-supply-following-chiropractic-adjustment-in-a-nursing-mother-of-twins-a-case-report-review-of-the-literature/

144   Heise, A. M., & Wiessinger, D. (2011). Dysphoric milk ejection reflex: A case report. International breastfeeding journal, 6(1), 6. https://doi.org/10.1186/1746-4358-6-6

sustainable and natural and begin making small changes. Results will come with time, but changes may be dramatic and immediate. Maybe mom's skin is a little clearer or dad's stomach isn't so sensitive to certain foods. There may be less seasonal allergy symptoms in the home or maybe it's easier to lose or gain weight as each body requires. And if this is occurring in such a short time, imagine how much benefit baby will receive because of the decision to lower the "body burden" of a plastic and preservative-laden world. It's worth it!

Now that we've explored ways to declutter the body's neuroendocrine system as well as connect and optimized the nervous system, the master system in the body, it's time to discuss birth as it relates to breastfeeding. Labor and delivery are where this orchestra reaches its greatest crescendo. It's the foundation to the important work of building a baby, which society has somehow been conditioned to believe ends with birth and is to be outsourced to formula industries and pediatric offices thereafter. On the contrary. This is when these systems are fully operational, online, and primed for growth.

This is not the time to disband the birth team. Our job is just beginning to equip a brand-new nervous system with nutrition and connection. So many of these hormonal queues and nutrient pathways we've been focusing on for months leading up to this are just now starting to activate and yield results. But labor and delivery, as currently normalized and standardized, is shutting these down. It's stacking the odds in favor of the "house". Too many mothers are entering a roulette game of birth interventions, and they need to know how to exit the casino floor, because this is not a game. The stakes are way too high to go in without a plan, or to navigate it alone.

SIX:
CONNECTED BIRTH:
THE FOUNDATION OF WELL-FED BABIES

THE CULTURAL PERCEPTION OF BIRTH

Birth is amazing. It's powerful and unmatched in the biological world. It's where the best of physical nature meets the most innately maternal and spiritual instincts. It's something that is at once so commonplace and standardized in our society, and at the same time, so mysterious and even misunderstood, that we have a lot of research to do to better support it. The physical act of giving birth is driven by hormones. This delicate cascade is easily and far too often disrupted by modern practices and approaches to birth in this country. Based on the sheer numbers related to the uses of interventions during labor and delivery, it's apparent that our doctors enter the delivery room expecting trouble. They perform "routine" procedures in an effort to have a padding of hospital policy to fall back on, should something go wrong. The ironic thing is that it usually does, because of what is occurring. It's a self-fulfilling prophecy of catastrophe and emergency C-sections.

In any disciplinary review, in malpractice claims or after-action reviews, if a doctor can show that they did what was "standard care" for their industry, and if their peers can attest they would have done the same thing in similar circumstances, the system sides with the status quo. But that same system is failing. We expect better outcomes, lower Cesarean rates, higher successful breastfeeding initiation, duration, and exclusivity. We should have lower infant mortality rates, fewer deaths to SIDS, with the correct number being exactly zero, and fewer cases of crippling postpartum depression. We should see fewer infections, prescriptions, admissions, and interventions. The reality of these current trends do little to instill confidence that our birthing industry has it all figured out.

One of the contributing factors is the fact that most families interact with this system briefly, and only a few times, over their lifetimes. The miracle of adding a new member to the family overpowers the whirlwind of the unfamiliar and the chaotic memory of each one's delivery. The craziness, the excitement, the intervention is expected and even celebrated in the comedy that comes with memory of such a happy event. Unless something goes wrong.

When it comes to hospital births, *safety* is their primary selling point. They want to be entrusted with the birth because of their track record. They have the experts on stand-by in close proximity to the state-of-the-art equipment, all primed, sterilized, and ready to go. Nobody ever plans to have an *unsafe* birth, of course, but when they zoom out slightly and look at the entirety of the birth picture, we start to see practices, outcomes, and systems that are unsafe. Suboptimal.

These unsafe practices can be subdivided into "dangerous", and "harmful". Popular culture and current messaging around birth has already painted the vivid, traumatizing picture of what a *dangerous* birth looks like- far away from the bright lights of a delivery table, not a single stirrup in sight. No doctors checking cervical dilation, no comforting beeping sounds of heart rate monitoring. Far away from the bright labels and sickly, sweet scent of fresh formula powder. Nobody is wearing scrubs, masks, and gloves.

This terrifying imagery from Hollywood films distracts the narrative away from the "harmful" aspects of current birthing practices. These are things that lead mothers to make statements like "Thank goodness they were able to get me in for an emergency C-section when they did," or "Some babies don't need that intervention, but the doctors said mine was the worst they had ever seen." These are unplanned, unwanted interventions that lead to a shutdown of mother's supply, or that permanently alter how a perfectly-formed new little human being is first forced to interact with their environment – their food, their sleep, their bond with mom. These are "harmful" outcomes from the birth process, but the fact that they are not fatal, we are led to believe we dodged a bullet. Something akin to Stockholm's syndrome can creep into some family's perspectives if they're not careful. Some come to view the broken system as their savior, rather than their captor.

It is important to remember at this point all birth workers cannot be painted with a broad brush. There are absolute heroes that work in labor and delivery every day. These are disciplined, compassionate, and principled obstetricians, nurses, midwives, and other care providers who have truly mastered their art and are some of the bravest and best in their fields. In no way is this meant to single out any field of medicine, any method of birthing practice, or any one philosophy. There is a beautiful and necessary blend of expertise, from the receptionist at a hospital, to the anesthetist in the OR, to the doula at the bedside that all touch a part of this miraculous event called birth.

But with a system so firmly entrenched, with so many variables and actors in play, it's easy to forget that there is an inherent element of risk, there is danger, and there is harm that can often happen when we dismiss nature. Risk must be accepted, on some level. Its weight, its gravity is felt by all entering the sacred space of birth. But empowered mothers cannot afford to enter its domain. Families can't afford to be fearful when they have the option of being prepared. They can choose to be informed instead of intimidated. Every care provider who accepts the assignment and steps into that room is the sum total of every patient they have ever cared for before. Every clinical victory and every tragic loss. They are also human, and they carry some element of their life story, their own biases and fears as well as their inherent strengths and tools, into that delivery room. Choose your providers and your birth team well, because their philosophy as they enter that realm will become your philosophy. Their fears can become your interventions. But their expertise and calm will also become your support.

THE PARACHUTE PLAN

Imagine preparing to go skydiving with ten people. They're all experienced thrill seekers and adrenaline junkies. On the beautiful flight up, you take in the beach and the mountains far below. The blue sky is everywhere. Some part of your stomach is gripped with that visceral feeling of anticipation, what some call fear, but you trust the training, the equipment, the pilot, and maybe you've even done a jump or two before.

As you prepare for the jump, you learn that three of the ten packs are not parachutes, but ordinary backpacks. This is admittedly a terrifying prospect. But let's examine why. Is skydiving risky? Absolutely. Everyone knows and accepts that climbing onto the plane. Is it dangerous? No. If it was, only a few of the absolute craziest people would ever do it. If you talk to anyone who has ever completed a jump, they describe the thrill of the experience enthusiastically. And every single person who has survived would assure you it isn't dangerous.

That's because the people who don't believe it to be dangerous are the only ones around to tell you that it isn't.

That's the difference between *dangerous* and *harmful*, of *safe* and *unsafe*, and the nature of risk itself. Currently, the system shepherds many moms onto a plane. They trust the pilot and the plane as it makes a nine-month long climb to the delivery jump. But roughly three parachutes nationally aren't deploying properly, and in some hospitals, as many as seven of these chutes are defective.[145] Our metaphor breaks down here, because it does not mean that seven in ten deliveries end in a fatal fall. These instead end in emergency surgical birth interventions, in unplanned Cesarean births.

Birth is not some skydiving experience. It isn't a plane to jump out of, pull on a cord with a prayer and wait and see if anything deploys. It's a series of intentional steps that every member of the birth team can make. Our culture seems to prefer the "wait and see" method, and when mom's chute fails to open for the myriad of reasons we will discuss here, and then some, we rush her into surgery.

Mothers are the pilots here. More than that, they have wings and nature has given them the power of flight in the birth world. They were designed to soar through labor, not fall until a parachute of medicalized birth interventions deploys. We expect parachutes to catch us when all else fails, but to intentionally jump out without a plan, with what we hope is a functioning parachute but nearly 30%[146] of the time is not- that's risky. That's harmful. But it's also been normalized, in our birth culture.

It's time to give mothers back the controls. Plans change. Engines fail and parachutes tangle. We can embrace the beauty of

145 Kozhimannil, K. B., Xu, X., & Glance, L. G. (2013, March 1). *Cesarean delivery rates vary tenfold among us hospitals; reducing variation may address quality and cost issues: Health Affairs Journal.* Health Affairs. Retrieved September 1, 2022, from https://www.healthaffairs.org/doi/10.1377/hlthaff.2012.1030

146 Cesarean Rates. (n.d.). Retrieved September 1, 2022, from https://www.cesareanrates.org/

the flight while still preparing for the possibilities of the unplanned. For example, if an unplanned Cesarean is the end result, despite all our best intentions, we can do so much to recover and reclaim the power of connection, even in the midst of the supreme intervention. In America, 86% of babies are separated from mother for the first hour following a Cesarean birth. For mothers who elect to be in the 14% that receive "couplet care", or "kangaroo care", or skin-to-skin contact, and have early and continuous contact with their baby, their chances of successfully breastfeeding exclusively at 6 months double.[147] They can recover from a turbulent flight, a failed parachute deployment, and a rough landing. They can mourn the parts that didn't go as planned, celebrate the ones that did, and pour everything else into connecting and caring for this tiny new human.

WHAT DOES INTERVENTION MEAN?

Things that seem so normal and "routine" to our culture are far from natural. Interventions interrupt what is biologically routine during childbirth. The word intervention is, by definition, "the systematic process... to remediate or prevent a... problem." It also refers in medicine to "an act that alters the course of a disease, injury, or condition..." And almost comically, "a planned, often unannounced meeting with a person with a serious personal problem... in order to persuade the person to seek treatment."[148] A personal problem like having an eight-pound human wedged in one's pelvis, perhaps?

Since these procedures are so ingrained in the society at this point, parents are made to feel reckless or backwards if they refuse

---

147   Charmatz, H. (2014, May 4). *Can hospitals keep moms and babies together after a cesarean?* SF Birth Doula Heather Charmatz. Retrieved September 1, 2022, from https://sfbirthdoulaandplacentaencapsulationservices.com/birth-blog/2014/5/3/can-hospitals-keep-moms-and-babies-together-after-a-cesarean

148   Harper Collins Publishers. (n.d.). *The American Heritage Dictionary Entry: Intervention.* American Heritage Dictionary Entry: intervention. Retrieved August 16, 2022, from https://ahdictionary.com/word/search.html?q=intervention

them. This is not so. Every patient is well within their rights to ask why something is happening, explore options, and they can always decline any procedure. This is why interviewing healthcare providers and selecting a birth team is so important beforehand to enhance communication as things are underway. Be aware of who is allowed in that sacred space. If a doula or midwife is bringing their fear into that room, address it. If a doctor or nurse makes the mother feel ignored or invalidated, she can ask for other help. Mother is the one in charge, and parents are the ones ultimately calling the shots for their baby.

When someone mentions interventions during delivery, it calls to mind the image of forceps, vacuum extraction, Cesareans, membrane rupture, and episiotomies. Many may not realize that continuous fetal heart monitoring, IV fluids, and epidurals are also major disruptors to the natural progression of labor. Even restricting what mom can eat or drink, or how she must be positioned are big interferences. When doctors say *intervention*, what so often is meant is *interference*.

When the neuroendocrine connection is intact and clear, the central nervous system is running the show, and the chemical orchestra is in tune and building to a crescendo. Mother and baby engage in an innately coordinated process to initiate labor. Baby positions herself appropriately, and mother's body begins to release key hormones like oxytocin, prolactin, and relaxin to prepare for labor and lactation. Her body becomes more finely attuned to this towards the end of pregnancy, as greater amounts of oxytocin act on the uterus. This allows it to soften, *efface*, and *dilate*.

Oxytocin, as mentioned previously, is responsible for the wave-like contractions of the uterus muscles for labor. The uterus is what is called a *smooth muscle*, meaning it responds to chemical signals rather than conventional nerve pathways like skeletal muscles do. Skeletal muscles can be contracted consciously, but smooth muscle is more reliant on chemical and endocrine signals to perform its function. Contractions increase in strength as labor progresses, gradually reaching peak levels. This also coincides with peak levels of labor pain. When this happens, the brain will release endorphins, the feel-good chemical. Some mothers describe this as deep meditation, a natural high, and say it is one of the most transformative and spiritual experiences of their lives. Towards the end of labor, a particular class of stress hormone called catecholamines will flood her system. Even for an exhausted mother after long labor, they function like a boost of adrenaline. They wake her up, so she is alert and ready to meet baby and begin breastfeeding. The levels of oxytocin climb and maintain that loving, connecting bond between mother and baby.

DEFINING AN INTENTIONAL BIRTH

When events transpire in this way and are allowed to happen on mom and baby's timelines rather than the hospital's schedule or the provider's shift, the likelihood of medically necessary interventions drops. There are five major areas where medical practices diverge from the evidence in how we approach birth.

1. Allowing labor to begin and progress naturally

2. Permitting mother to move freely and labor as her body directs

3. Supporting mother emotionally and defending against doubt

4. Encouraging pushing spontaneously and intuitively, and

5. Keeping mother and baby together continuously

These five elements make excellent "mile markers" on the birth mapping process. The starvingbabies.com website includes free resources to begin this conversation. Discussing these concepts with your birth team and keeping plans in mind that honor each of these points is a great way to feel prepared and in sync with your birth supporters. Various interventions often fall under each of these five categories.

For example, many mothers have scheduled inductions at 39-40 weeks of pregnancy. Remember a due date is simply an estimation, and it is normal to deliver three weeks prior to, or two weeks after your "date". It's an estimation, made at best, based on mother's last menstrual period or the size of the baby on ultrasound. The American College of Obstetricians and Gynecology does not consider a pregnancy "postterm" until after 42 weeks.[149] In a country like the United States, where women are frequently induced at 39 and 40 weeks of gestation, this makes 42 weeks seem considerably longer. It's perfectly within nature's timeline even if it doesn't fit the current cultural paradigm. It allows more time for baby's lungs to develop and for hormonal labor to begin naturally. Many births are already doomed to interventions simply by being induced with artificial, or synthetic oxytocin, like Pitocin. Pitocin is not the same thing as oxytocin.

LABORING NATURALLY

In the fast-paced hospital world, labor is a slow and deliberate process. This poses a serious inconvenience to medical personnel and support staff, who are often caring for multiple patients across various stages of labor, each at their own, deliberate pace. In an attempt to standardize deliveries, induction has become commonplace. Even in women who begin labor naturally, the process is helped along by two main interferences: the administration of Pitocin or synthetic oxytocin, and membrane rupture, also called amniotomy.

It is perfectly natural for first-time mothers may be in "latent" labor for over twenty hours, or for experienced moms more than fourteen

149   *When pregnancy goes past your due date.* The American College of Obstetricians and Gynecology. (n.d.). Retrieved August 16, 2022, from https://www.acog.org/womens-health/faqs/when-pregnancy-goes-past-your-due-date

hours. Dilation of six centimeters (6 cm) is generally the threshold for *active labor*, and labor is considered "stalled" or "arrested" if her water has broken at or beyond this point with no progress for four hours of active contractions, or six hours after receiving Pitocin without any progress. Feeling a little overwhelmed by all these rules? These are the categories and standards that the medical world has established for themselves, and every attempt will be made to ensure mother's body follows these timelines.

Labor should be allowed to develop naturally, and not necessarily on a doctor's timeline. When women are admitted early on during latent labor, the likelihood of all interventions and ultimately, the risk of ending up with a Cesarean birth all increase.[150] The longer a mother is sitting in a bed, surrounded by people being paid to find something wrong, the longer the likelihood that they will.

Natural labor may take a while, and that's perfectly okay. It means everyone needs to practice a bit of patience and understanding as mom and baby get on the same page neurologically. This is probably easier to do if mom chooses to labor at home for a while, or chooses a midwife-assisted birth, because she is close to her own shower and tub, her fridge of food, and her own bed with her Netflix. She isn't interrupted by strangers rushing in and out of her room, checking her cervix and lecturing her about not eating or drinking in case she needs a surgical procedure from the 1940s. (More explanation on this in a moment.)

This is a great time to involve the doula, if mom has chosen to include on, in the monitoring progress and keeping mother calm and engaged. This is an excellent opportunity to receive a gentle, specific chiropractic adjustment to put the nervous system in control again. This slow start to labor also helps the tissues around the birth canal

---

150   Marowitz A. (2014). Caring for women in early labor: can we delay admission and meet women's needs? *Journal of midwifery & women's health, 59*(6), 645–650. https://doi.org/10.1111/jmwh.12252

begin to stretch and accommodate the changes, which leads to less likelihood of tearing. She may apply some oils or massage the area to ease the tension and stretching that occurs. Mother's nervous system may choose to speed labor along or slow it down for a while. That's the natural wisdom of birth acting through mother's nervous system, and it's okay. It's to be honored, defended, and celebrated for doing what it is inherently designed to do. She may choose to express some of the colostrum in preparation for delivery, which is one way of supporting the oxytocin release.

Amniotomy, or membrane rupture, is also referred to as "having the water broken". In some hospitals this intervention is even routine. Many women do not even know the procedure has been done to them. Once the membranes are ruptured, the risk of infection begins, and complications with fetal heart rate and umbilical cord issues set in. There is also an increased risk of malposition for the baby. An important independent research review, called the Cochrane Library, looked at labor of 5,583 women across 15 different studies involving women who began labor naturally and those who "had their water broken". They concluded that routine amniotomy showed no shortening of first stage labor and a probable increase in the likelihood of unintended C-section delivery.[151] Even in women with prolonged labor, the evidence does not support breaking the waters as a routine interference. Having the water break is not even a pre-requisite for a healthy birth, and some women deliver baby in a fully intact amniotic sac.

The use of Pitocin to induce or augment labor also poses serious risks. Contractions are stronger, harder, and continuous. Mother's system doesn't have sufficient time to rest between contractions, as it does with her own oxytocin. Pitocin lacks the neurological intelligence

151   Smyth R., Markham C., Dowswell T. (2013). Amniotomy for shortening spontaneous labour. Cochrane
       Database of Systematic Reviews, (6), CD006167. 10.1002/14651858.CD006167.pub4 Retrieved from
       http://onlinelibrary.wiley.com/doi/10.1002/14651858.CD006167.pub4/full

that mother's own endocrine system shows. Pitocin labor increases the strain on the muscle that is the uterus. Usually, to manage the pain and side effects of Pitocin-induced contractions, an epidural is also required. Some mothers express their desire not to have Pitocin for labor. But once baby arrives, it is usually administered for what is called *active management* of the delivery of the placenta. Another term to be aware of is *prophylactic uterotonic*. This injection usually happens so fast, and often via the IV line that is already running, that many mothers don't have time to give adequate consent until it's underway. This interference also defeats the initial intention of allowing mom's own oxytocin to birth the placenta. Sometimes nurses will offer *fundal massage* or will pull the umbilical cord to speed things up, called *controlled cord traction*. Providers are taught this will reduce the likelihood of postpartum hemorrhage, but the data simply does not support this practice of pulling on the cord or pressing on the uterus. Research is severely lacking on the use of pulling the cord without using Pitocin or the use of fundal massage for any reason[152]. Nevertheless, this is standard practice. It's normal procedure. It also may be completely unfounded, misguided, and unnecessary for a particular mother's unique birth.

Slow labor can be helped along by walking, resting, or receiving chiropractic care. Manually expressing breastmilk can also increase oxytocin release and prepare the colostrum supply for the incoming human. We need to normalize these non-medical, non-surgical, drug-free measures before turning to the "standard" interferences.

---

152 Hofmeyr, G. J., Mshweshwe, N. T., & Gülmezoglu, A. M. (2015). Controlled cord traction for the third stage of labour. *The Cochrane database of systematic reviews*, 1(1), CD008020. https://doi.org/10.1002/14651858.CD008020.pub2

FREEDOM OF MOVEMENT/EATING

Mother should be allowed to move freely. She should be allowed to eat and drink. The need to fast before delivery is so often "standard practice" in hospitals. It's based on guidelines from the 1940s, when patients under general anesthesia were observed to become nauseous and vomit, sometimes aspirating into their lungs and developing pneumonia. Current surgical practices protect the airway from this happening now, and the likelihood of needing to undergo general anesthesia, instead of just a nerve block, is very low. Research has shown too that the stomach is never truly empty, so we might as well let mom fill it with healthy snacks to keep her happy and energized. The World Health Organization[153] and the American College of Nurse-Midwives[154] agree. Yet the American College of Obstetricians and Gynecologists[155] and the American Society of Anesthesia[156] still hold to this outdated practice of restricting women to clear liquids. Instead of encouraging mom to eat and drink, we routinely start an IV to keep her hydrated.

INTRAVENOUS FLUIDS

Administering IV fluids during labor increases the water weight of mother and baby. It can cause nipples to become difficult for baby to latch onto. IVs containing glucose cause high blood sugar in mother and baby, and low blood sugar in the newly delivered newborn[157] after the sugar crash. Baby is weighed immediately, since modern

---

153   World Health Organization (1996). Care in normal birth: A practical guide. Geneva, Switzerland: Author;
      Retrieved from http://whqlibdoc.who.int/hq/1996/WHO_FRH_MSM_96.24.pdf
154   American College of Nurse Midwives (2008). Providing oral nutrition to women in labor. Clinical
      Bulletin Number 10. Journal of Midwifery & Women's Health, 53, 276–283.
155   American College of Obstetricians and Gynecologists (2009a). ACOG Committee Opinion No. 441: Oral
      intake during labor. Obstetrics and Gynecology, 114(3), 714.
156   American Society of Anesthesia (2007). Practice guidelines for obstetric anesthesia: An updated report
      by the American Society of Anesthesiologists Task Force on Obstetric Anesthesia. Anesthesiology,
      106(4), 843–863.
157   Goer H., Romano A. (2012). Optimal care in childbirth: The case for a physiologic approach. Seattle, WA:
      Classic Day.

birth seems obsessed with birth weight in this country. After baby eliminates much of the water weight out in the first diaper, the pediatrician often pulls out a trusty "Enfamil Growth Chart" and shakes their head concernedly. They often recommend "supplementing" or "topping off" with formula until baby's weight is back on track. See how the system works? One paper found that excessive fluids in labor can affect breastfeeding.[158] Despite there being slender evidence of an upside, and substantial evidence of downsides, some 62% of women receive intravenous fluids during labor.[159] It's standard procedure to keep mom hydrated and her blood sugar up, they say.

ELECTRONIC FETAL MONITORING (EFM)

In the 1970s, fetal monitoring became a standard practice that was touted as a way to reduce infant mortality. There was no evidence to back up this claim, but it quickly replaced the practice of listening to the baby's heartbeat with a conventional stethoscope. This is one of a long list of skills that many doctors graduating from medical school today have chosen to outsource to technology. While there was no proven decrease in infant mortality, there was a noted increase in mothers needing C-sections and instrumental vaginal births. This is believed to be due to the lack of mother's freedom of movement during labor, or a mother's inability to use birthing tubs, balls, or positioning to relieve labor pain. A recent discovery in the *Journal of Legal Medicine* found that a large reason for the increased Cesarean rate is more likely due to the interpretation of the data from fetal monitoring, than to actual medical necessity. The false-positive prediction for fetal distress rates using this form of heartrate monitoring is greater

---

158   Kujawa-Myles, S., Noel-Weiss, J., Dunn, S., Peterson, W. E., & Cotterman, K. J. (2015). Maternal intravenous fluids and postpartum breast changes: a pilot observational study. International breastfeeding journal, 10, 18. https://doi.org/10.1186/s13006-015-0043-8

159   Declercq E., Sakala C., Corry M., Applebaum S., Herrlich A. (2013). Listening to mothers III: Pregnancy and childbirth. New York, NY: Childbirth Connection.

than 99%. It has greatly contributed to unnecessary C-sections and their accompanying risks, and it has not demonstrated its claimed efficiency in reducing infant mortality. "Any other medical procedure with such an abysmal pedigree would have gone the way of bleeding by medieval barbers,"[160] the report states, tongue-in-cheek.

Many doctors will point to hospital policy, feeling that the EFM provides them a level of protection from lawsuit. Stanford Law Review found the opposite to be true, however. Having a continuous, permanent record of the fetal heartrate through delivery may increase the risk to the hospital of a lawsuit, because it becomes more a question of the doctor's interpretation of the data. The other option instead of EFM is what is known as *intermittent auscultation*, which is the tried-and-true method of using the stethoscope occasionally to check fetal heartrate. This is the recommendation of the American College of Obstetricians and Gynecologists as well as the Association of Women's Health, Obstetric, and Neonatal Nursing. For healthy women with no suspected complications, auscultation, using the stethoscope, is an equally acceptable standard of care. Admission test strips to determine baseline fetal heart rate, are also not proving to be necessary. If there is a medical reason, telemetry can be used instead. Your birth provider should know what this request means. This will allow mom to move freely during labor.

Again, for those entering a delivery ward looking for a problem, waiting for an insurance-funded intervention that involves risk, they will often find one. These are conversations that expectant mothers and concerned fathers may choose to have with their providers before the heat of labor is on and the clock is running. Emotions will be high and if the decisions and desires have been discussed beforehand, it frees up mental and emotional energy to support mother rather than Googling terms on the phone in the corner.

160   Sartwelle T. (2012). Electronic fetal monitoring: A bridge too far. Journal of Legal Medicine, 33, 313–379.

EPIDURALS

Women choose to receive epidurals to decrease pain levels. Pain is a highly individual concept, and every mother has different thresholds and perceives it in different ways. This is a highly personal area that should be affirmed and supported as she makes her own decisions.

Without the pain of contractions and delivery, however, oxytocin levels drop. This usually results in stalled labor, which usually requires augmentation with Pitocin to resume uterine contractions. Pitocin is different from the body's naturally produced oxytocin, however, as it does not cross the blood-brain barrier. It therefore can't release the endorphin rush described at the beginning of this chapter, meaning mother never reaches that euphoric, dreamlike state prior to delivery. The epidural blocks the pain signal, which may afford some relief from the constant contraction of Pitocin, but it also shuts down the cascade of oxytocin, endorphins, and catecholamines, all of nature's signal chemicals.

Epidurals also causes the pelvic muscles to relax, since mother can no longer directly activate these skeletal muscles. The Pitocin is the gas pedal on the uterine contractions, and the epidural is the break on those postural, pelvic muscles. These are an important part of helping the baby to turn and descend through the birth canal, since they are untethered from the nervous system while the anesthesia is in effect.

Epidurals can also cause fevers, which has historically led to separation of mother and baby for evaluations. In our COVID-traumatized medical world, this could lead to full-blown quarantine measures until symptoms pass and negative test results return. During the critical hours after delivery, time is of the essence. Such separation devastates the chances of successfully breastfeeding.

One other seldom discussed fact is that epidurals contain fentanyl. This appears to be one of the main culprits in increased risks of early breastfeeding problems[161].

Remember that mom is calling the shots during labor and delivery. If she decides she needs an epidural, the available evidence favors a low-dose, anesthetic-only and encourages her to adopt a side-lying or upright position to decrease the need for instrument-assisted delivery. If at all possible, waiting until active labor is underway, when she is approximately 6 cm dilated, will improve the chances of baby having good position and engagement in the birth canal as well as decrease the likelihood of an epidural fever.[162] Discuss with your care provider the options beforehand of receiving an epidural. Consider their recommendation if mother does spike a small fever during delivery and ensure she will not be quarantined or isolated against her will. Since many hospital policies also require other interventions like IV fluids, electronic fetal monitoring, and restricted movement with an epidural, explore your options of foregoing these measures.

MOVING FREELY

Without the electronic fetal monitor or IV equipment, mother should be able to move freely. She can walk, kneel, sway, stand, lie, or crouch however her body dictates. She should have ample room and be given the ability to move as she needs throughout labor. Many will choose to have a shower, soak in a bath, or support themselves on cushions or a ball to allow themselves the freedom of moving and laboring in various positions. The father, a doula, or a birth chiropractor may help if she asks for back rubs or sacral support during her labor.

---

161   Goer H., Romano A. (2012). Optimal care in childbirth: The case for a physiologic approach. Seattle, WA: Classic Day.

162   Lothian J. A. (2014). Healthy birth practice #4: avoid interventions unless they are medically necessary. The Journal of perinatal education, 23(4), 198–206. https://doi.org/10.1891/1058-1243.23.4.198

SUPPORTING EMOTIONALLY

So much of what occurs in the birth process is regulated and perceived from a subconscious, primal part of mom and baby's neurology. Mother may know that she is in a safe hospital room, consciously. She may recognize her husband, or her midwife or OB consciously. But the moment her finely attuned system senses doubt, a simple look or a comment, an exasperated sigh or shrug, the subconscious, primal part of her system will go into defense and protection mode. It may pause labor or stall the let-down of her milk supply until it feels safe again. Remember these reflexes and instincts are so hardwired in her system, it takes a while for the signal to reach the deep programming from her conscious mind. The setting is vital, and the attitude of the birth team sets the tone for a natural, connected delivery. Mother's mindset can set the trajectory at the outset. Choosing to place familiar pictures, setting intentions, playing music, providing blessings or prayers or repeating mantras can all keep this system in a confident, protected space.

KEEPING MOTHER AND BABY IN CONTACT CONTINUOUSLY

Babies are not starving for nutrients. They are starving for connection. They are deprived of care, not calories. When considering breastfeeding, what occurs there is far more about neurology than nutrition. The nervous system needs to be restored to the crux of the conversation surrounding breastfeeding, and its effect on the endocrine system needs to be strengthened and protected. Parents and providers alike need to look to the labor and delivery process as the primary juncture for either supporting or derailing the natural cues to breastfeeding. Our current model is too often operating outside evidence-based care. This isn't the scientific approach we often hear touted from medical academia. Hospital policies often recommends certain things because they work best for their system. And that system has been so shaped and incentivized by formula manufacturers and insurance companies.

For example, the American Academy of Pediatrics agrees with the World Health Organization on the importance of skin-to-skin contact. Seldom, though, does such an agreement manifest in the actual practice during birth. This is especially crucial during what birth research refers to as the sensitive period of postpartum care, that critical hour following delivery when connection and proximity is so crucial. Some hospitals committed to research-based obstetrics are designated as "baby friendly" facilities. They are adamant about not separating mother and child. Instead, they allow them to bond skin-to-skin, a practice also called *kangaroo care*.

Skin-to-skin care is a huge and important piece of the birth puzzle that is often missing in the transition to breastfeeding. It is what the name implies, placing the naked newborn against mother or father's bare chest and covering them in a blanket to keep them warm and dry. Placing baby on a towel or hospital gown is not the same thing. This should be practiced as soon as possible after birth, and for as long and as often as possible thereafter, especially up until the first feeding is complete. Mother's cortisol levels, one hormone that indicates stress, lower in response to the amount of skin-to-skin time she has with her baby. The longer the time she connects with baby, the lower the median level of stress-hormone present in her system. Skin-to-skin contact also reduces the time before placental delivery.[163] It reduces the risk of postpartum bleeding.[164]

Separating mothers and babies is a uniquely human behavior. And it is distinctly modern. Everything we do in the research world

163   Marin Gabriel MA, Llana Martin I, Lopez Escobar A, Fernandez Villalba E, Romero Blanco I, Touza Pol P. Randomized controlled trial of early skin-to-skin contact: effects on the mother and the newborn. *Acta Paediatrica*. 2010;Vol. 99(issue 11):1630–4.
164   Dordevic G, Jovanovic B, Dordevic M. An early contact with the baby - benefit for the mother. *Medicina Preglio*. 2008;61(11-12):576–9.

is assuming this is the norm. Every study is viewed through the lens of separation after birth. When we perform research on the effects of skin-to-skin contact, we treat separation as the normal control group, and skin-to-skin as the experiment. Yet when we study animal behaviors, we treat contact with newborns as the standard.[165] It wasn't until the use of general anesthesia in the early part of this century that we routinely separated mothers and babies. Now that we no longer us general anesthesia as the standard practice, it is time to rethink the separation of mothers and newborns after birth. This still occurs in an average of 20% of births. It varies significantly depending on regional practices too. Three-quarters of hospitals surveyed in Mississippi for example, separated mom and baby for more than an hour after birth. In New Hampshire, Vermont, and Rhode Island, that rate was 0%. Every hospital surveyed in those states affirmed skin-to-skin care after uncomplicated, vaginal births.

Rates of "couplet care", of not separating mothers and babies after birth are doubling.[166] The system is improving and the needle is steadily moving towards what research has always told shown to be the best option. However, when Cesarean births occur, this separation occurs in three-quarters of cases. When one-third of births in this country are Cesarean, this means that too many mothers are delaying that bonding time and losing precious percentage points for successful breastfeeding likelihood. Mothers who participate in skin-to-skin bonding are 50% more likely to exclusively breastfeed at six months.

Since such a large number of surgical births are occurring, and since the benefits of skin-to-skin contact is so well-documented, it is

165 Moore, E. R., Anderson, G. C., Bergman, N., & Dowswell, T. (2012). Early skin-to-skin contact for mothers and their healthy newborn infants. The Cochrane database of systematic reviews, 5(5), CD003519. https://doi.org/10.1002/14651858.CD003519.pub3

166 Boundy, E. O., Perrine, C. G., Barrera, C. M., Li, R., & Hamner, H. C. (2018). Trends in Maternity Care Practice Skin-to-Skin Contact Indicators: United States, 2007-2015. Breastfeeding medicine : the official journal of the Academy of Breastfeeding Medicine, 13(5), 381–387. https://doi.org/10.1089/bfm.2018.0035

worth considering ways that mom and baby can initiate skin contact immediately after even such a major procedure. One of the reasons hospitals are hesitant to do so is fear of hypothermia. Operating rooms are kept cooler to discourage bacterial growth and blood flow. Anesthesia often lowers body temperature for mother too, so a combination of the two make them worry that baby will be too cold. Research is showing that babies who participate in skin-to-skin contact within the first hour following a Cesarean birth are not at any increased risk of hypothermia.[167]

This question of whether or not a hospital allows *post-Cesarean couplet care* can be addressed with the doctor or hospital administration prior to labor. Even in circumstances where a C-section delivery is not the desired birth experience, it would be worth the effort of having a conversation to explore options and may be a determining factor in mother's chosen birth location. A C-section birth plan, the "Parachute Plan" is available on the *starvingbabies.com* website to be downloaded and given to the surgical team as a part of the birth map, should this scenario present itself.

The benefits of delayed cord clamping are also well-documented and are worth a discussion. These benefits are seldom observed in hospital deliveries out of necessity for the delivering doctor or staff. Thirty to sixty seconds is the American norm for what they consider *delayed clamping*, which is up from ten seconds in previous years[168], but still below what research is defining as "delayed". The World Health Organization recommends "late cord clamping (performed approximately 1-3 min after birth)" for all births.[169] And the American

167 Gouchon, S., Gregori, D., Picotto, A., Patrucco, G., Nangeroni, M., & Di Giulio, P. (2010). Skin-to-skin contact after cesarean delivery: an experimental study. Nursing research, 59(2), 78–84. https://doi.org/10.1097/NNR.0b013e3181d1a8bc

168 Cleveland Clinic. (2021, December 22). *Delayed cord clamping: How long, benefits & risks.* Cleveland Clinic. Retrieved August 16, 2022, from https://health.clevelandclinic.org/what-you-should-know-about-delayed-cord-clamping-after-birth/

169 WHO. Guideline: Delayed umbilical cord clamping for improved maternal and infant health and nutrition outcomes. Geneva: World Health Organization; 2014.

College of Nurse-Midwives says that five minutes is appropriate if a full-term newborn is placed skin-to-skin. There is no documented increased risk to mother or baby, and there is a significant reduction in intraventricular hemorrhage or the need for blood transfusions in preterm babies.[170]

Some mothers choose to wait until the cord is completely depleted of its supply, when it stops pulsating and turns white, and all the stem cell rich blood is in the baby. After all, what is the rush? Baby may need time to activate the rooting reflex that leads them to crawl up mom's belly to the breast. These are crucial milestones in the delivery and convalescent journey for mother and infant.

During pregnancy, the areolas tend to darken, effectively painting a bullseye around the nipple for eyes that are first learning to lead a baby to latch. The medical assembly line of standardized delivery has been taught to smear antibiotic ointment on these new lids, as a routine procedure and protection against the risk of chlamydia. This ointment blurs vision, making it harder to locate and blunting the activation of this latch locating reflex. Unless mother is facing an active case of chlamydia, there is very little evidence for the medical necessity of this practice.

Sometimes it takes baby a little longer to make the transition from water to air. If their umbilical cord is attached, they are oxygenating as they have for the past nine months. We are so quick to aspirate, stimulate, and separate. There is a common theory taking root that baby will intentionally tuck the umbilical cord under their chin, or even wrap it around their neck to protect that vital blood supply in the immense pressure of the birth canal. While the image looks concerning, a baby who is not yet breathing air is likely not being

---

170 ACNM. (2014). *Delayed umbilical cord clamping - American College of Nurse Midwives.* Retrieved August 17, 2022, from https://www.midwife.org/ACNM/files/ACNMLibraryData/ UPLOADFILENAME/000000000290/Delayed-Umbilical-Cord-Clamping-May-2014.pdf

strangulated by the cord. Obstetricians and midwives are specially trained to manage this aspect of the delivery process and know what to watch for.

CONNECTED BIRTH

After birth crying stops, babies will undergo a short period of relaxation and then become alert. They will actively move their head and limbs and begin moving their mouth. They begin actively rooting for the breast, look at mother's face, and make determined movements toward the breast. They may bring their hand to their mouth and make small movements without moving or rocking. They then begin to crawl and push, slide, or wiggle to shift themselves toward the nipple while making "soliciting" sounds. They may pause for a time between stages. Once they find the breast, they will become familiar with the areola and begin to massage or root on the breast before finally latching at the nipple. After self-attaching and suckling to their satisfaction, they should finally sleep.[171] This all occurs during that vital first hour post-delivery. When one third of babies are being delivered via C-section, this first hour is often spent separated, as the medical team does what it has been trained to do. They are checking baby and monitoring mother and offering the best care they know how. Everyone is busy testing, washing, tending to baby, filling out paperwork and maybe even bottle-feeding the newborn. It all looks very urgent and official.

This is having a catastrophic effect on mother's supply and nervous system, but it is also terrifying to the newborn's system. Mother's conscious brain knows baby is fine, but her body's primitive reflexes, the deep programming, feels it may have lost the baby. This is the time

---

171   Widström, A. M., Lilja, G., Aaltomaa-Michalias, P., Dahllöf, A., Lintula, M., & Nissen, E. (2011). Newborn behaviour to locate the breast when skin-to-skin: a possible method for enabling early self-regulation. Acta paediatrica (Oslo, Norway : 1992), 100(1), 79–85. https://doi.org/10.1111/j.1651-2227.2010.01983.x

for mother to gently remind them of her duty to also offer baby the best that she can. She is the only one that can provide that presence and contact. She can count toes and wait to poke and prod her baby until that time passes. Once the brand-new heartbeat has slowed, once their breathing is in sync and baby has had their first meal at the breast, then the hospital can resume whatever parts of their process the parents have consented to.

One study found that mothers send up to 30 text messages within the first two hours of delivery, and this did not include photos and updates on social media sites.[172] The use of smartphones and distracted mothers is considered a risk factor in multiple reports, and is becoming so common, it is now referred to as *maternal distraction*,[173] and is affecting research outcomes and infant health. If a mother chooses to share this sacred time with family, friends, or the social media world at large, she might consider having someone else oversee documenting and communicating this journey if it must be done in live time. If it can wait, please consider the tradeoff. There is so much more to learn about this process, but technological distraction may be seriously affecting hormone levels and critical bonding time. Tragically, there are even documented cases of infant fatalities while mom is distracted by her smartphone.[174]

Human babies are the most neurologically fragile infants among the primate world. They have limited sensory input. They have very underdeveloped systems for dealing with the adaptive stress of birth. Imagine the stress of being tugged from the warm comfort of a womb,

172   Pejovic, N. J., & Herlenius, E. (2013). Unexpected collapse of healthy newborn infants: risk factors, supervision and hypothermia treatment. Acta paediatrica (Oslo, Norway : 1992), 102(7), 680–688. https://doi.org/10.1111/apa.12244

173   Rodriguez, N. A., Hageman, J. R., & Pellerite, M. (2018, May 18). *Maternal distraction from smartphone use: a potential risk factor for sudden unexpected postnatal collapse of the newborn.* Retrieved September 1, 2022, from https://doi.org/10.1016/j.jpeds.2018.04.031

174   Pejovic, N. J., & Herlenius, E. (2013). Unexpected collapse of healthy newborn infants: risk factors, supervision and hypothermia treatment. Acta paediatrica (Oslo, Norway : 1992), 102(7), 680–688. https://doi.org/10.1111/apa.12244

being rubbed until they cry, scrubbed down, swaddled, fed, all this while being rushed around under fluorescent lighting, surrounded by strangers and invasive smells and sounds.

Contrast that with baby being placed on the mother's abdomen, the place it has known for the last nine months. The cord would be allowed to deliver its final blood flow to the tiny body. Baby takes their first breaths and makes the first cries.

The newborn then exercises the most supreme of the primitive reflexes, as it begins a crawl up mother's body and latches itself at the breast to begin stimulating the flow of colostrum. The neurology of this tiny system craves the creation of a microenvironment. Baby's world must expand slowly, from the womb to the size of mother's body. It is safe within the bosom and in constant contact with the skin flora. The warmth and steady, familiar breathing and heartbeat of mother slows baby's heartbeat. It eases the transition from womb to world. It allows both nervous systems to exit the sympathetic, "fight or flight" state of delivery together. They return to normal, baseline, "rest and digest" mode, called the parasympathetic state.

This sort of constant contact alters the physiological response of both bodies. A flood of endorphins and oxytocin bathe both systems. This establishes the crucial bond that can only happen immediately after delivery. The oxytocin assists in concluding labor. It can help return the uterus to its normal size and tone. It returns blood pressure and breathing to normal levels for mother. It's the precious feedback signal to the orchestra conductor that mother delivered a viable, perfect little human. It's the hormonal applause from a packed house and a thrilled audience.

After baby's arrival, after the cord is clamped, the placenta delivered, baby is latched, the connection and proximity of "rooming in", of engaging in skin-to-skin contact continues. It will reinforce the background biology of both mom and baby that they are safe and connected to each other. Her supply flourishes, and baby's nursing reflexes reinforce lactation, and drive supply. Hormones normalize and tell mother her baby is safe and nourished. This all helps reduce the risk of postpartum depression. This is when dad can also participate in the kangaroo care, especially if mom is feeling "touched out" or needs a rest.

THE VERNIX

Around nineteen weeks of development, baby begins to form a layer on the skin called *vernix caseosa*, it's the white, waxy substance that protects the skin in utero. Closer to delivery, this substance starts to mix with the amniotic fluid, and baby will swallow some of it, which is suspected to help establish healthy gut bacteria. It also makes it easier for baby to slide along the birth canal, and the vernix contains ingredients that help mom heal after a vaginal delivery. The World Health Organization recommends leaving this vernix on the skin for at least six hours, but even up to 24 hours after delivery. It is a powerful mixture of specialized cells and oil secretion that protects this baby's skin and helps it establish healthy bacterial cultures.

If baby passes the meconium during delivery, or mother has an amniotic infection, it is best to bathe baby sooner to avoid the risk of bacterial infection. And for babies born later in pregnancy, this vernix may have washed off or already been absorbed, and baby's skin may be slightly wrinkled. That's okay too. Discussing delayed washing with the birth team is a great conversation to have before baby arrives. It's okay to delay the social media photo shoot until later if it means baby's skin can benefit from vernix contact and skin-to-skin time with mother. The baby's head will emit that "newborn smell" that many mothers are familiar with. If she has elected a scent-free journey, of purging fragrances and phthalates from her environment, this subtle, sweet smell will trigger more hormonal response in her body. Placing a beanie on the baby's head will block these smell receptors and may affect her let-down response. Mom and baby can use their senses of smell to deepen the response and connection and rushing to wash this off and slather baby in soap may be a detriment to the power of smell.

KEEPING MOTHER AND BABY CENTRAL

"Baby Friendly Hospitals" and birthing centers understand this sacred chemistry. They do not separate mother from infant. After securing this designation for the maternity care centers in their country, Sweden saw the six-month success rate of breastfeeding reach 75%.[175] Contrast that with the United States' current 25%,[176] and we see that Baby-Friendly Hospitals are a major contributor to breastfeeding-friendly birthing.

Many well-intentioned nurses enter the profession because they enjoy being around newborns. An increasing number of Labor and Delivery wards see the power of birth. These brave nurse advocates are winning a long battle. They take pride in cleaning, swaddling, and feeding the new arrivals. Unchecked, however, this can lead to a medical phenomenon that has been half-jokingly called *"Whose Baby?" Syndrome.*

The delivering doctor considers the child as under his medical charge during labor. Once delivery is over, the nurses swoop in. They have far more experience in all their tasks than a first-time mother. They're immediately viewed as the experts and authorities on the care

---

175   Hofvander Y. (2005). Breastfeeding and the Baby Friendly Hospitals Initiative (BFHI): organization, response and outcome in Sweden and other countries. Acta paediatrica (Oslo, Norway : 1992), 94(8), 1012–1016. https://doi.org/10.1111/j.1651-2227.2005.tb02038.x

176   Centers for Disease Control and Prevention. (2021, November 24). *Breastfeeding Report Card.* Centers for Disease Control and Prevention. Retrieved August 23, 2022, from https://www.cdc.gov/breastfeeding/data/reportcard.htm

of the newborn. If left unchecked, this is neither helpful nor empowering to a new mother already overwhelmed with raising this newborn. Now she feels the pressure of feeding it, changing a diaper, and swaddling. She needs affirmation and guidance, not a replacement caregiver or separation. The time may come when she needs such help, but the initial experience is critical in forging that bond.

At a time when the birth providers should be rallying around a new mother to continue her efforts to feed and calm her newborn and herself, too many of them are separating. When she is struggling with postpartum stress, anxiety, depression, the general response is to take her baby away and wish her well on her way back to work. *We "delivered" this baby*, the system seems to say. *We will feed it, supervise it, and tell you all the ways it deviates from our expectations. We will train its frail and flawed immune system and we will let it self-soothe in the darkness of its separate room. You just rest. You need to go back to your regular life. You need to take care of you.*

Sometimes taking the best care of herself involves comforting, feeding, calming, and being present for the baby. Motherhood is the most supremely unselfish act in humanity, and to expect mother to feel comfortable in separation and selfishness is to diminish her power. There is an important balance to be struck in the vital support of self-care, of resting and reassuring her, but also of allowing her to establish her competence and connection with her newborn.

The best birthing outcomes feature delivery staff dedicated to championing mother, giving her small, simple cues as the baby is ready for them. The paradigm shift is huge, but it is crucial for facilities who truly wish to celebrate and honor the power of connected birth. Those who respect the autonomy and supremacy of the mother-infant bond see the best birth outcomes.

CO-SLEEPING

Another uniquely American aspect of new baby arrival is the general lack of co-sleeping. Everywhere else in the world and throughout most of history, this practice is simply known as "sleeping." A recent blitz by the mainstream media has terrified mothers about the risk of smothering their children. Self-proclaimed experts repeatedly warn that cribs are the best places for babies, ideally in a separate room.

This imitates nothing in nature. We repeatedly see co-sleeping has been the practice of the most mentally stable cultures and the majority of human experience since the beginning of time. It is the natural way to fend off predators and protect the baby. It is also the way to provide the best access to food supply. Risks materialize when the philosophy is mixed and matched, because while parents are free and obligated to choose their approach to these issues, they are not allowed to select the consequences of those choices.

When a baby has free access to the breast throughout the night, we begin to prime a mechanism called the "appestat". This is a recently described section of the brain that acts like a thermostat, but for appetite. It's a new area of intense research and important possibilities in understanding the baby's relationship with food over the course of their life. It teaches the baby that food is readily and constantly available. If they aren't completely hungry, or once they are full enough, they can stop nursing, and can resume again whenever they need. This keeps the food-seeking, survival portion of their nervous system, the "fight or flight" portion of it, turned down. It keeps them in a constant state of resting and digesting.

During the night, when baby feels hungry, they are very adept at navigating to the breast in the dark. They will often latch spontaneously, even without waking mother. If for no other reason than to "comfort feed" they draw small amounts of milk. This stimulates milk production and keeps mother and infant in this parasympathetic, rest zone. Preferring a nipple over a pacifier is also important biological feedback. It reminds mother's body of the necessity of milk production for this tiny human. They are working their latch muscles and coordinating that on the breast, and not on a synthetic rubber nipple.

Co-sleeping with a baby who has been formula fed often disrupts the satiety hormone levels. These chemical signals make baby feel full for longer. Since formula digests far more slowly than breastmilk, it sits in the gut for a long time and keeps baby full throughout the night. They generally don't wake to feed or comfort suckle, and that leads to higher instances of SIDS. In some of the documented tragedies where babies were "smothered", substance use by the mother, sleep aids, drugs, or alcohol were involved, or the baby was exclusively formula fed. They aren't constantly waking to stimulate production or latch spontaneously.

This is not a manual for co-sleeping, and every family situation is different. It is a practice that deserves to be seriously investigated with the partner before baby arrives. There are multiple benefits of co-sleeping on sleep schedules, hormone levels, nervous system activity, and more. It is currently considered counterculture. But it is so important in developing a stronger bond with baby and parents. It's returning to the natural circadian rhythm of our ancestors.

ADDRESSING LATCH ISSUES WITH A LACTATION EXPERT

Occasionally mother-baby dyads face difficulty establishing a latch. Some possible correlation exists between the frequency of latch issues, like lip or tongue ties, and decreased levels of Vitamin B9. Tongue ties occur when the connection between the tongue and the bottom of the baby's mouth is too far forward for comfortable movement and latching. It is a concern only when it affects the function of the baby's mouth in forming a healthy latch and suckling during feeds.

This issue can be addressed prior to pregnancy as well. With some education, preparation, and supplementation where needed, many latch issues might be avoided with the proper intake of B9. A symmetrical roof of the mouth, and lips and tongues that are free to flare open and draw in the nipple properly and fully will help avoid painful nursing. While there is a time and a place for assessment and intervention of latch-related issues, prevention is always best. Research is still being done, but some studies are suggesting a link between B9 deficiency and the occurrence of lip or tongue ties. Interestingly enough, folic acid is present in certain flours, starches, and byproducts like flour. A deficiency in quality folic acid may explain why mothers sometimes crave these types of foods during their first trimester, as their body attempts to address its own shortage. Too much of the "unmethylated" form of folic acid is not good. This is an excellent thing to discuss with a nutritionist or healthcare provider, especially if the mother has a metabolic disorder like MTHFR. She will want to ensure her body is utilizing all the vitamins she is offering it in the healthiest, most available form for her and baby's bodies.

It's important to note that many people use the terms "folic acid" and folate interchangeably. They are not the same.[177] Folic acid is the synthetic form of folate, and as mentioned, some women have genetic conditions that prohibit them from utilizing the synthetic form. It's a great time to consume liver and other organ meats and dark, leafy vegetables to boost natural folate levels.

The presence of a lip, tongue, or cheek (also called a buccal) tie does not necessarily require a surgical intervention. Sometimes simply learning to reposition the baby to improve the latch or receiving "body

---

177   Arnarson, A., & Meeks, S. (2022, March 17). *Folic acid vs. folate - what's the difference?* Healthline. Retrieved August 11, 2022, from https://www.healthline.com/nutrition/folic-acid-vs-folate#vitamin-b-9

work" from a trained and qualified pediatric chiropractor, lactation consultant, or pediatric dentist can address the issue and optimize the latch without surgical release of the tongue-tie. If mother decides that surgery is needed, it is critical that she find a provider who will help her perform the stretches and exercises necessary to prevent the tie from reforming. Once the tissue has reattached and scarred over, it can be more difficult to correct and needs to be addressed completely and proactively the first time. It is always okay to ask for a second opinion, especially from a qualified provider or lactation consultant before deciding.

HIGH LIPASE LEVELS

For mothers who make the commendable decision to pump and store their breastmilk for baby, another important piece of information may become relevant. Breastmilk and saliva contain an enzyme called lipase. Enzymes are chemicals that initiate chemical reactions and break down certain substances. Lipase works on fats and oils that are present in breastmilk.

Sometimes a mother will produce milk that contains a greater amount of lipase. If she chooses to store this milk, there is a possibility that it spoils quicker than previous pumps, because the lipase goes to work immediately. She can sample this by taste, or by smell. If the breastmilk she intends to feed to baby smells old, soapy, or rancid, if it has a grey or bluish tint, even if she recently pumped it, she may have elevated lipase levels. While mother is producing high lipase breastmilk, it can be scalded (heated to just below the boiling point) once it is freshly pumped. Heating it helps to inactivate the lipase enzyme. If the baby seems fussy upon feeding, has an abnormal amount of colic or gas after eating, elevated lipase may be the cause. There are excellent tutorials in how to salvage stored milk with elevated lipase, and scalding freshly pumped milk usually helps it store better for longer.

Proximity and bond drive milk supply. Our birthing practices encourage immediate separation, cord clamping, isolation, and provoked anxiety. They do little to address the needs of the newest nervous system, or to encourage mom's natural biology from instigating milk flow. Parents are bombarded with formula messaging, with free samples. They face the pressure of medical expertise and society discouraging breastfeeding. In all the rush of baby showers, OB appointments, wellness checks, and so on, moms have little time to sit and just be. They need time to bond with their baby, away from social media and texts.

Indeed, from the moment a woman is "diagnosed" as being pregnant, the medical industrial complex snaps into action. It is aided and abetted by the social media monarchs. The data points from her excited posts and family engagement land in the lap of every formula marketing machine willing to pay for these leads. She becomes a line item on a spreadsheet, a blip on social media radar to be marketed to, relentlessly.

She'll see surveys from these companies, dressed up as a request for information, or quizzes about what kind of formula is right for her baby. This type of messaging will gradually, imperceptibly shift her focus. It is intended to move her from middle ground or undecided to firmly within the mindset of the formula consumer. Once she learns to recognize the programming, these tactics are quaint and almost comical. But for those who have never stopped to question the paradigm, these concepts are foreign, almost threatening.

CHOOSING TO BECOME AGENTS OF CHANGE

Faced with the reality of what parents are up against, it is easy to feel dwarfed and powerless. Those who choose to trust in nature are fighting a trillion-dollar agenda and a pharmaceutical juggernaut whose existence depends on trusting them. They hold entire countries hostage with shortages, fabricated research, shredded evidence, and extorted fortunes. Entire nations rely on their products for their infants to survive. The only way to leave the system is to refuse to play the game. Turn off the media messages of inadequacy, the fear-mongering and pandemic porn that has come to define so much of the way society operates today.

It's time to find those friends and family members who value free speech and medical autonomy above all else. Those who are willing to research and wrestle with hard data, to reach tough conclusions and make difficult decisions. These parents refuse to give in to the psychological conditioning and the mass formation psychosis. They call out and shut down the fearmongering, the gaslighting, and virtue signaling, whether it comes from a family barbecue or the pediatrician's office. They can do it politely, confidently, and firmly, when they have the data on their side. They choose to be surrounded by like-minded people, those committed to toxin-free, drug and surgery-free approaches to living wherever possible. They value the elegant and divine design of the human body.

Humans are not a weak species. Humanity has not existed and thrived on this planet for so many millennia by depending on chemical cocktails to update our immune system, or surgical procedures to correct what our fledgling science believes nature got wrong. Every new intervention has results and outcomes that speak for themselves.

This tribe of truth-seeking, nature-trusting parents approach birth with the same confidence and reverence for life. It's the same peace found in a mother who supports her nervous system, first and foremost. That is the master system of the body. It directs everything else. She has cleared out her endocrine system from the noise and distractions of modern cosmetics, detergents, sanitizers, and preservatives. And she has prepared her immune system for defense with proper diet, exercise, and healthy exposure to sunlight. She doesn't coddle it, but she supports it.

This group of like-minded believers shows up at the delivery room or the birthing center in the dark hours of the early morning to welcome in an equally strong, resilient newborn. This baby has survived nine months of miraculous incubation and is now permitted to make its journey into mortality on its own terms and timetable. There is patience and persistence as labor progresses naturally. It is all coordinated with a clear neuroendocrine connection. Baby emerges and is immediately and irrevocably placed on the body that bore it, built it, and is best equipped to feed it.

It may struggle momentarily in its new waterless microenvironment to climb and latch at the nearest breast. This activates a flood of reflexes, hormones, and impulses that the tiny system expects to feel connected and nourished from its earliest moments. Mother experiences a flood of emotions, a chemical cascade that helps her heal fully from the traumatic miracle of childbirth. Eventually the umbilical cord, that physiological bridge from mother to baby, the link between womb and world is delicately removed. From then on, baby is reliant on mother's milk for everything that blood flow used to provide: nutrition, immunity, and neuroendocrine signals of safety and satiety.

Constant proximity and persistent latching establish the supply of colostrum, the nutrient dense milk. This is a living tissue packed with essential additives as Mother Nature sees fit. Its job is to cultivate the seedling digestive system into a robust and resilient mechanism for growing a healthy body. Eventually, baby will try simple, healthy foods. They add this to the foundational nutrient, breastmilk. For at least the first year or two, the cornerstone of that child's health can and ought to be nature's ultimate food source.

It must be acknowledged, of course, that not every story ends with such a happily ever after. Illness, complications, intervention, trauma, and tragedy occur at every stage of the human journey. But these are the exceptions that make the majority so miraculous. They are opportunities to grieve and console one another as humans have done for as long as we have shared this planet with each other. These are opportunities to hold space and withhold judgment or criticism, to shut down feelings of doubt and inadequacy. There are fears and guilt we heap upon ourselves for things so firmly beyond our control. There are illusions we subscribe to about what we are able to predict and prevent. As a country, the United States is convinced they can outspend and out-treat the consequences of unresearched interventions. These may be causing more harm than help. The cost paid in sick and starving babies is far too high and has been normalized for far too long. The system is not winning the war for well-fed, well-connected babies, and the societal and medical evidence is piling high around us.

No longer can families expect to enter an optimal pregnancy while limiting the mother's role to a nine-month commitment followed by a passive participant in labor. They can no longer view the father's involvement as minimal, optional, or non-existent. If employers, legislators, and families took the approach of birth providers elsewhere in the developed world, the nation would see optimal outcomes grow by leaps and bounds. Raising a child truly takes a village.

A $100 billion industry will not turn on a dime, and it will not die overnight or without a fight. It may take generations. It may require decades of focus and commitment to truly empowering mothers in their birth journeys. This is Cronos, the Greek titan that holds Rhea's babies captive until she feeds it a stone. Until she wakes up and reclaims her power, and those children return to fight against the giant. It may take a decade, as it did in the legend of Zeus and Cronos, but the struggle is worth the freedom that awaits.

Generational changes happen in incremental, tiny decisions. They happen in conversations like the one this book is intended to spark. They happen when grandmothers share lost wisdom and insight with the next generation willing to listen and act. They begin when mothers walk out of formula aisles in droves, when they march to their legislators' offices to demand honesty and accountability from their government and the companies it pretends to regulate, when they have the courage and the research to tell their medical provider "no thank you" to a procedure that seems as innocuous and "standard procedure" as any they have learned in medical school. Birth and breastfeeding are not a "one-size-fits-all" approach, and our care shouldn't be either.

This change costs dearly. It represents early morning feedings when nipples are chapped and bleeding and both mom and baby are crying out in frustration and pain. But it pays richly. It is the truly settled feeling in quiet moments where both are bonding together, the thrill of silently celebrating a full latch and an effective transfer. One by one, we loosen the stranglehold on our economy and our national health. Every statistic matters. We can begin the long trek up the charts, away from the highest infant mortality in the developed world. We can reclaim our place as the freest, healthiest, and most self-sufficient country.

This is where mothers and grandmothers can and ought to shine. This is where lactation consultants and midwives can ask permission to enter the conversation and to be a lifesaver. We need people who believe in the power of birth and the necessity of breastfeeding to help rescue this new mom and baby from a system that is waiting for her to fail. It waits for those newborn screams for food at 2 am, for frustrated tears from mom. It wants its product within arm's reach. "*Just once. Just for now,*" it seems to say. "*You're cracked and bleeding and this will fix it,*" And one bottle becomes two, becomes the norm. The baby's system instantly craves the sweeteners and the thickeners and the ease of the latex nipple. It ignores the colostrum and the human supply. It's the mother's first blow of crushing inadequacy, her first experience of rejection from her child. It's the baby's first exposure to a highly processed, calorie-dense and nutritionally deficient diet, the beginning of the decline of their shared immunity, their first experience being left alone in the dark with a bottle of formula instead of lying between a sleeping mother and father. Eventually, they nurse themselves into a milk-coma. They sleep so deeply, and they wake less often. Their risk of SIDS doubles.[178]

Pause here and breathe. Consciously take a moment to release the fear, shame, and guilt. If walls go up, and swords slide through scabbards, sheath them. Take a moment to drop those defenses and listen. Not to this text, but to that innate surety deep within that reaffirms adequacy and courage. Be brave enough to consider the message without perceiving it as an attempt to control or threaten any part of the beautiful, parental autonomy.

This is all so emotionally charged and may be triggering for those reeling from devastating losses and fears. Feeling inadequacy, blame or doubt, are not worthwhile burdens to carry. There are invaluable resources available for mothers working to regain emotional footing, self-confidence, and mental resilience through these struggles. This book is here to shore up, to remind mothers of their crucial worth and

---

178   Stuebe A. (2009). The Risks of Not Breastfeeding For Mothers And Infants. Reviews In Obstetrics & Gynecology, 2(4), 222–231.

innate capacity to connect and nurture. It is here to remind fathers of the sanctity of their role as provider and protector, of the support and advocacy they can claim during the birth and breastfeeding journey. This culture needs to continue to discuss postpartum depression. Rather than filing down and softening every sharp edge of this birth journey, we need to lean into the hard conversations, the evidence of connected, powerful births. Collectively, there is a growing need to acknowledge the loss and trauma of miscarriages, of losing milk supply, of separation and complication. There is an unfathomable toll that these stressors take on mothers well beyond the acceptable, "normal" grieving period. There is space here to accept the challenges and trauma of motherhood without shaming those who feel it most acutely.

This book is not to pressure anyone into anything that is not well within their natural desire to offer their child. We must brave deeper discussions and investigation of the ideal in order to understand how far we have drifted from it. Most of the birth interventions we have devised are to alleviate the natural discomfort of childbirth: early inductions, epidurals with actively managed labor, expedited clamping, washing and swaddling, formula supplementation or exclusive bottle feeding, breast pumping, self-soothing training, and physical separation as mom returns to work. All of these minimize the impact on mother's life of the biggest decision of her life: that of becoming a parent. It's leading to increasingly disconnected children who trade emotional dependency for chemical dependency from the womb.

The coping mechanisms we then seek and hear about in the fourth trimester onward are our attempt to course correct long after deviation from nature has occurred. Many books and pediatricians preach much-needed reminders of self-love, self-acceptance, and mental health as the top priority. It certainly is for the mother. It's an essential part of any approach to birth. But self-love alone is not enough. Prioritizing mother's comfort, convenience, and lifestyle above all else is disconnecting babies from birth, the benefits of breastfeeding, and of neonatal neurology.

Baby needs mother's body to feed and feel safe, just as they have needed her body to build their own. They have sacrificed so much to bring a new life into the world, and every effort must be honored and cherished. Now, a village stands at the ready to help her raise this child, but the task isn't done. The father, the aunts and grandparents, the doula and midwife, the doctors are all needed now in their various capacities. Mothers ought to be able to lean on them without hesitation and reservation. She must have confidence in their approach, in the alignment of their philosophy with hers. This is not the time for her to feel she needs to pull away, because she didn't come this far just to come this far. Too many babies are getting off the mom train at the birth station, and are being left behind in nutrition, immune development, and neurology.

The psychology of pro-formula advertising is so subtle. They say, "breast is best" and quickly escort you back into your comfort zone. During COVID, they targeted 2.67 billion customers, posting around 90 times per day[179]. This has given them record facetime with their could-be customers to sew seeds of discouragement. *Anyone who encourages you to do otherwise is attacking you,* they say. *Do what's easy. Breastfeeding just isn't for you. You don't make enough. Your baby prefers our product. They have a milk allergy. Your lifestyle requires this. Anyone who says otherwise is shaming and belittling you. Reject them. Feel attacked. Fire your doctor if they push you to breastfeed and you don't want to.*

---

179   Shea, D. (2022, April 28). *WHO reveals shocking extent of exploitative formula milk marketing.* Univadis. Retrieved August 10, 2022, from https://www.univadis.it/viewarticle/who-reveals-shocking-extent-of-exploitative-formula-milk-marketing-764711

Ironically, those are the same voices that urge you to blindly follow their advice if they want to induce labor or recommend supplementing with formula. The information just presented is pro-breastfeeding. It does not seek to manipulate or mandate. It strives to be as far from shaming or guilt-tripping as it can possibly be written. It is educating and empowering. It sees every parent as an intelligent, capable human who can entertain all the nuances and embrace all the variations of normal. They can navigate these with grace and autonomy together. It does not consider them so programmed that a position on breastfeeding is inherently triggering and ostracizing. Moms are smarter than to be made to feel victimized. They too want to have connected births and ease into ideal breastfeeding. They don't have to feel inadequate because nobody explained the tradeoffs to them. Reject affirmation from a system that has repeatedly, and in some instances, intentionally, failed to support these crucial paradigms.

Please prioritize mental and physical health. Do not misunderstand or minimize the importance of that. Mother's mental wellbeing is crucial for the health and energy needed to care for this newborn. Read affirming, self-care books and do what is necessary to keep moving forward. Learn to accept best efforts, and judge on intention. Release any expectations that hold mother hostage to the desires and motives of others.

At the same time, recognize the incredible potential that lies within her power. Understand how vital the parental decision to leave a toxic manufactured environment will be for a growing family. It's a conscious decision to begin now to take small measures to prepare and prevent more than they may have ever realized they could.

A mother may want with everything in her to nurse her baby for two years. Know that whatever effort and energy she bravely brings to this endeavor, it is far better than what she is currently being told. Set small milestones along the way and celebrate them with those she chooses to share them with. This isn't making unrealistic expectations; it's planning for success and moving forward with confidence in the direction of her dreams for her newborn.

The movement to diagnose pregnancy, to medicalize the delivery process, to numb the pain of childbirth are not in mother and baby's best interest, despite what the current narrative claims. The attempt to replace mother's body with a plastic bottle full of watered-down corn syrup and chemicals is not how nature intended this process to work. This isn't feeding babies, in the truest sense of the word. It isn't the lactation consultant's fault. It's the product of a cultural assault on what nature has primed mothers inherently to do.

Fighting for this reality begins long before a positive pregnancy test. It can begin before conception. It begins with a committed partner and a birth tribe who is willing to work and save and support this new human, to keep mother alive and loved throughout this journey. It begins in weekly grocery trips when she chooses increasingly clean foods and toxin-free products. It's when families get intentional with what water they drink. It's when they consult doulas, a midwife, an OB, a birth chiropractor, and the rest of their birth team. Include them in the parts of the birth plan they touch, and the things that matter most to mother, who is at the center of this journey. These victories can begin again fresh every day, as new developments and plot twists inevitably occur. New choices and circumstances push her towards the goal, around new obstacles and on to new challenges. Love guides through that process, and don't lose sight of the goal. A well-connected birth, a successful breastfed infancy, a return to a normal routine, to physical intimacy with your partner, to social time with friends, those will come. Although she may occasionally feel differently, mothers are not pregnant and breastfeeding forever. Choose to find the joy in this time. Realize current decisions have far-reaching effects. It's worth it to hold on a little longer.

Mother needs to see to her own needs, which don't evaporate with baby's arrival. The current narrative from formula companies and birth businesses does not use this in a "self-care" sense of the word. It views her as a means of constructing a physical specimen, one that is expected to dispense a functional human on their schedule and timeline. It's a society that has made a pact with Big Bottle, Big Food, and Big Pharma, which have all purchased and are protecting one another. When a mother stays connected, when she asserts her maternal right to that child, she threatens that dynamic. No longer is she merely a human builder, she becomes a child bearer. She is a force to be reckoned with, a gatekeeper whose approval and trust must be won over through persuasion instead of by coercion. Her permission must be obtained through dialogue rather than assumption. There is something fiercely and femininely divine in that mission of motherhood. Something that threatens their design to separate, to manipulate, and to profit from starvation.

Imagine that first-time mother again. What if someone takes the time to explain to her before pregnancy all that is at stake here? What if that formula isn't on the hospital bedstand? Would this world be different? What if a specially trained birth chiropractor offers a supremely gentle adjustment to a minutes-old nervous system? What if she and her husband draw that crying baby in close, skin-to-skin to slow its heart rate? What if she gently brings it to her breast, feeling the tiny, heaving breaths slow. She can relish that feeling of connection and know that she is needed by this child. The baby feels the security of her presence. Something so familiar for the last nine months slows the hunger and the panic and the disconnect this tiny body is expressing through its cries. To that tiny human, and to the entire world, she is enough.

INDEX

GLOSSARY

Active Labor	Typically defined as 6 cm cervical dilation with productive contractions
Amniotomy	The intentional rupturing of the amniotic sac, with the intention of inducing or speeding up labor. Also referred to as Artificial Rupture of Membranes (AROM) or more commonly "breaking waters".
Anorexia	A lack of appetite
Appestat	A region of the brain believed to regulate appetite, food-seeking, intake, and feeding behaviors. This is still the subject of active study.
Autonomic Nervous System	The part of the nervous system that is beyond conscious control. It innervates smooth and cardiac muscles, glandular tissue, and governs involuntary actions. It is commonly divided into "parasympathetic" and "sympathetic" parts, the rest/digest, and fight/flight modes.
Bartter Syndrome	A rare genetic disorder that was the subject of the misdiagnosis in the early part of the electrolyte imbalance study of 1979.
Bilirubin	Latin for "red bile", it is an orangish waste product that forms with the breakdown of red blood cells. Elevated levels of bilirubin can result in jaundice.
Blood Breast/Brain Barrier	The natural protective mechanism that prevents unwanted substances from leaving the bloodstream in breast or brain tissue to avoid contaminating sensitive tissues.
Body Burden	The amount of a particular toxin that can be stored or detoxified out of the body at a particular time. Body burden often depends on the type of toxin, the length of time of the exposure to it, the timing of the exposure and the dosage or amount absorbed by the body.

Breastfeeding	The process of feeding a baby from a mother's breast. A breastfed infant, for purposes of research and discussion initiates feeding within one hour of delivery, maintains exclusive intake of breastmilk for the first six months of life, and continues to nurse from the mother for the first year (AAP) or two (WHO) of life, while adding other foods and liquids after the six month mark.
Casein	A white, tasteless protein that comes from milk after contacting rennin. See also Whey
Catecholamines	A class of neurotransmitters, or chemical signal hormones that act on the nervous system. This includes amines like epinephrine, norepinephrine, and dopamine. They assist in the concluding portion of labor to keep mother alert and awake as she finishes delivery and transitions to post-partum care for baby.
Central Nervous System (CNS)	The brain and spinal cord, the "master system" of the body. Its function is to perceive its environment and coordinate the appropriate response of all the cells in the body.
Cesarean Delivery	Also called a C-Section. Delivery of a baby by a surgical operation that opens the abdominal wall and the uterus. So named after a belief that the emperor Julius Cesar was born that way.
Chloride Deficiency	Also called hypochloremia, it is an electrolyte imbalance that affects the circulatory system and the body's ability to regulate, store, or excrete water. This was the subject of the 1979 investigations that gave rise to the Infant Formula Act of 1980.
Colostrum	Also called "first milk", it is the earliest form of breastmilk to arrive around the time of delivery. It is characterized by the high protein and antibody content, the dense nutritional profile, and the thicker, white or yellowish fluid. It is very effective at boosting infant immune function, digestive health, and may act as a laxative for the meconium.

Connected Birth	The *Starving Babies'* philosophy of allowing mother autonomy over birth with the intention of remaining connected to baby throughout labor and delivery. Connected birth plans honor the body's innate intelligence and prepare the nervous and endocrine systems of both baby and mother for successful recovery and recognition to provide the best opportunity for breastfeeding.
Controlled Cord Traction	A combination of techniques intended to reduce post-partum bleeding. May include the administration of drugs to manage placental delivery, clamping and cutting the umbilical cord, massaging the uterus, and tractioning or pulling on the cord to assist in the delivery of the placenta. This approach has not been viably established by research, and should be discussed with birth providers.
Cortisol	A steroid hormone released by the adrenal glands, often in response to stress or exertion.
Couplet Care	The practice of maintaining mother and baby in close or constant proximity to one another. Also known as "rooming-in", this is a foundational philosophy in baby-friendly, evidence-based birth institutions. See also Skin-to-Skin care.
Cronobacter Sakazakii	The name of the bacteria commonly causing contamination of powdered infant formula and thought to be the cause of some infectious outbreaks. Often found with Salmonella as well. This organism was blamed for the Sturgis factory shutdown, but no genetic link was established to prove it was the source of infectious fatalities.
Delayed Clamping	The practice of allowing optimal blood supply to transfer from mother to newborn through the placenta and umbilical cord before clamping and cutting the cord. The American College of Obstetricians and Gynecologists recommends thirty to sixty seconds for this transfer to occur, while the World Health Organization recommends "late cord clamping", of three minutes or more.
Detoxification	The natural process by which toxins are eliminated from the body. While many substances can support this process, the body can and must detoxify itself, primarily through the kidneys and liver via stool and urine, but also through the skin via sweat and other pathways.

Dilate	Often referred to cervical dilation during labor, this is the process of enlarging an opening and making it cause to expand. This is different from "effacement". (See also Efface) Dilation is often measured in centimeters, where effacement is conveyed in percentages.
Duration	In breastfeeding, duration refers to the length of time in weeks or months that mothers feed their babies. AAP recommends one year duration, and the WHO recommends two.
Effacement	Cervical effacement or ripening refers to the thinning of the cervix as baby prepares to exit the womb. The cervix often has a bottleneck shape of about four centimeters in length, and during labor, the baby's position will begin to shorten this bottleneck. It is often described in percentages, whereas dilation is expressed in centimeters.
Electronic Fetal Monitoring (EFM)	EFM is the use of an electronic fetal heart rate monitor, usually attached to elastic belts that keep the sensors against the mother's abdomen. This allows doctors to continuously monitor the baby's heart rate through delivery. The practice was intended to detect abnormal or stressed heart rates early, but no discernible benefit overall has been observed in research literature. This procedure may result in unwanted interventions and unnecessary procedures, like C-Sections.
Endocrine Disrupting Chemicals (EDCs)	A class of chemicals, also referred to as hormonally active agents, that may interfere with normal endocrine (chemical) signaling in the body. These toxins are more prevalent in modern products and many of them have unknown or unpublished risks to human health.
Endocrine System	A major messenger system for the body made up of feedback loops of hormones released from various glands and organs. This is controlled by the central nervous system and these chemical signals are released into tissues and the bloodstream to achieve a specific result.
Endorphins	Short for "endogenous morphine", meaning naturally occurring opioid that is produced and stored in the pituitary gland. These are the "feel-good" chemicals that are produced as labor progresses naturally, and the brain requires this hormone to manage pain levels.

Epidemic Intelligence Service (EIS)	A branch of the US Centers for Disease Control and Prevention (CDC) that investigates the spread of diseases. This was formed immediately following the soy-based formula scare of 1979, which led to the Infant Formula Act of 1980.
Evaporated Milk	A concentrated, unsweetened milk that is made by evaporating some of the water away from whole milk. Evaporated milk was used as a staple in infant feeding when formula was scarce or expensive. It was able to store for long periods, and the smaller curd size made it easier for sensitive babies to digest.
Exclusivity	In breastfeeding, this refers to the concept of utilizing breastmilk as the sole source of hydration and nutrition, meaning baby takes no other solids or liquids while breastfeeding. Both the AAP and WHO recommend exclusive breastfeeding for the first six months of life.
Failure to Thrive	Also referred to as weight faltering or faltering growth, this is a common way of indicating insufficient weight gain or growth in children. This diagnosis is often based on growth charts. If birth weight dips 7-10% after day 7, or if baby is not wetting their diapers around six times daily after day four, or if mother is not experiencing breast changes or engorgement, it may be an indicator to alert a pediatrician, lactation consultant, or other skilled birth provider is necessary.
Flora	The collection of bacteria and other microorganisms that are found on a particular host. This may refer to skin or gut flora, which is the population of germs that reside in those regions. A diverse and healthy population is essential for a robust immune system, and practices like vaginal delivery, delayed bathing, and breastfeeding helps maintain this flora in babies.
Formula	A manufactured food that is designed and marketed for the purpose of feeding babies and infants under 12 months of age. Often prepared in a bottle by adding water to a powdered supply.

Fundal massage	Also known as uterine massage, this technique is intended to reduce bleeding and cramping of the uterus and surrounding structures after delivery, and encourage it to return to its normal size and position. This practice however, has little to no evidence of its effectiveness in reducing postpartum bleeding and is often uncomfortable. It is important to discuss this practice with the birth team.
Glucocorticoid Regulated System	This is a portion of the endocrine system heavily affected by arsenic contamination, among other toxins, where dysfunction often can result in muscle loss, Type 2 diabetes, osteoporosis, and other problems with metabolism and weight management.
Homogenization	In dairy science, the process of heating milk to make the ingredients of it completely uniform in terms of particle size and fat globules.
Hypochloremic metabolic alkalosis	See also chloride deficiency. This was the official corrected diagnosis during the 1979 investigation of soy-based infant formulas. It is caused by an electrolyte imbalance and treatment includes increasing salt and water intake. No long-term harm was demonstrated in follow-up studies for the diagnosed infants.
Hypothalamus	Greek for "under the chamber", this is a vital portion of the brain that is often referred to as the master gland, since it initiates the hormone response of so many other pathways in the endocrine system.
Immunoglobulin A (IgA)	A class of antibody that plays an important role in protecting the mucous membranes of newborns. It is found in high concentrations in colostrum and breastmilk, but also in saliva, tears, and seat.
Initiation	In breastfeeding, initiation refers to allowing baby to latch directly to the breast within one hour following delivery with the intent of establishing breastmilk supply from mother and nutritional, immune, and neurological connection for baby.
Intermittent Auscultation	The practice of utilizing a stethoscope to monitor fetal heartbeat during delivery. This is an alternative to the often-utilized electronic fetal monitoring and is an acceptable standard of care both in the United States and internationally for mothers who decline EFM.

Intervention	Any act or procedure undertaken by a doctor or midwife to intervene in the progression of the birthing process. While interventions may be absolutely necessary for a safe delivery, many are not medically indicated and may lead to the need for further interventions. When selecting a healthcare provider or facility for birth, it's important to discuss the likelihood and appropriateness of birth interventions. See also Connected Birth.
Jaundice	Also called icterus, it is usually a yellow or orange color of the skin, particularly the whites of the eyes in an individual with too much bilirubin. See also Bilirubin
Kangaroo Care	(See Skin-to-Skin Care)
Lipase	A natural enzyme that helps to break down fats and oils. May occasionally be elevated in breastmilk that is pumped and stored, leading to premature breakdown of the milk fat.
Lymphocytes	Specialized white blood cells that produce antibodies and other important components for the immune system.
Mammary Biotechnology	An evolving field of science that seeks to replicate natural breastmilk production by isolating MECs to produce milk-like product in a specialized environment known as a bioreactor.
Mammary Epithelial Cells (MECs)	Specialized cells that are found in breast tissue that, when stimulated by hormones like prolactin, produce breastmilk from the bloodstream. These have recently become relevant in mammary biotechnology, as firms like Biomilq harvest, replicate, and stimulate them to produce lab-grown milk-like product.
Maternal Distraction	A recently-described phenomenon in birth and breastfeeding literature where the mother is distracted by technology, particularly texting and social media, with detrimental affects to infant health.
Meconium	The earliest stool passed by an infant shortly after birth. This dark greenish mass accumulates in the intestines during baby's development and is discharged by defecation. Colostrum is thought to be an effective laxative in encouraging this to pass.

Medical Autonomy	The basic and universal human right to make decisions about their medical care, as well as for that of those in their legal custody. This includes the foundational ethical principles of informed consent, patient privacy, and freedom of speech.
Medical Detailing	The practice of providing gifts and incentives to hospital administration and staff in order to promote a particular brand of formula or drug. This may include take-home baskets for parents as well, and is intended to provide the appearance of medical endorsement or confer authority to formula manufacturers or pharmaceutical companies, often in a healthcare environment, like a pediatrician's office or the delivery wing of a hospital.
Mothercraft Nurses	The controversial and since-disbanded practice of recruiting sales representatives, often dressed as medical nurses, to advertise formula brands to new mothers under the guise of patient education. The practice was discontinued after public outcry, and most formula companies have now simply hired the doctors themselves to sell their product.
Necrotizing Enterocolitis	An infection common in premature newborns who require feeding via a G-tube. Incidences of this infection were shown to be lower in babies who were fed breastmilk.
Nonconformity	Abbott Nutrition's terminology for batches that were contaminated with microorganisms or otherwise fell outside normal quality control standards.
Oxytocin	A major hormone produced by the hypothalamus that plays a critical role in social bonding, reproduction, labor and delivery, uterine contraction, lactation, and other aspects of human behavior. It is mimicked by Pitocin, but only true oxytocin is able to cross the blood-brain barrier to take effect in the critical brain structures on which it acts.
Panada	A bread soup commonly fed to infants in previous centuries, before the invention of formula. It was often made from toast crumbs or a flour base with water or broth to make it easy to swallow.
Pap	A soft, semiliquid food made from milk or water with bread, similar to Panada.

Pasteurization	The partial sterilization of milk with the intention of destroying harmful organisms without altering the core chemical makeup of the milk. Pasteurization can also extend the shelf life of milk but led to vitamin deficiency and a loss of some probiotic properties of milk. Raw milk is becoming popular once more, as modern access to refrigeration and medicine expands.
Pitocin	A synthetic form of oxytocin, often used to induce labor, speed up or intensify contractions, or used as a "uterotonic" in the active management of placental delivery following labor. Pitocin does not cross the blood-brain barrier, and hence does not have the same effects as naturally produced oxytocin.
Placental Barrier	The protective mechanism that keeps the womb and baby secure from contaminates and pathogens from the outside world.
Postterm Pregnancy	Defined as a woman who has not delivered her baby after 42 weeks of gestation. Postmature or postterm pregnancies carry some health risks for mother and baby.
Prolactin	A hormone messenger that causes mammary epithelial cells (MECs) to produce milk when supplied with blood supply.
Prophylactic Uterotonic	See also Pitocin. Commonly used to help the uterus return to its normal size and shape following delivery. The natural alternative to this intervention is oxytocin production and the initiation of breastfeeding.
Relaxin	A signaling hormone that causes ligaments and joints to become more mobile in preparation for labor and delivery. Typically, relaxin release begins after the twentieth week of gestation and relaxin levels peak around delivery. Relaxin will peak and decline during the duration of breastfeeding and returns to baseline levels after weaning.
Satiety	The sensation of feeling full after feeding.
Skeletal Muscle	Muscles in the body that can be consciously controlled, like those in the limbs and parts of the core. These differ from smooth muscles, like the uterus, or cardiac muscles, which have a different mechanism of activation.

Skin-To-Skin/Kangaroo Care	The practice of initiating direct skin-to-skin contact with the mother or father following delivery to provide nervous system and circulatory benefits, transfer healthy bacteria, and improve bonding and connection with the infant.
Smooth Muscle	In contrast to skeletal muscle, smooth muscles are often governed by the autonomic nervous system or endocrine system. They are not consciously controlled. See also Skeletal Muscle
Special Supplemental Nutrition Program for Women, Infants, and Children (WIC)	WIC is the federal welfare program for low-income families to receive infant formula. Although funded and administrated federally, it is negotiated between infant formula manufacturers and the states.
Spillover Effect	A financial phenomenon documented in the sale of non-reimbursable products related to infant formula feeding. Formula manufacturers to receive contracts can expect an increase in their other products, and often increase their price point accordingly.
Vernix Caseosa	The waxy, cheese-like, white covering that often coats a newborn at delivery. It protects the skin from the amniotic fluid during development, and prior to delivery, is often absorbed into the water and ingested by the infant. Believed to be helpful in establishing healthy gut flora, increasing lubrication for vaginal birth, and aiding in any rupture or injury incurred during birth.
Wet Nursing	The practice of having another woman, besides the mother, providing breastmilk for an infant. In antiquity, wet nurses were retained to feed children. In modernity, using donor breastmilk or receiving excess breastmilk from another mother's supply.
Whey	The liquid portion of milk that suspends casein and is separated out by contact with rennin or after curdling and straining milk.

REFERENCES

(2002, April 25). *RE: European commission Endocrine Disrupters developments (1)*.

Abbott Laboratories Sentenced for Misbranding Drug. (2012, October 2). *JUSTICE NEWS*. Retrieved August 10, 2022, from https://www.justice.gov/opa/pr/abbott-laboratories-sentenced-misbranding-drug.

Abbott Laboratories Stock Buybacks. Abbott Laboratories Stock Buybacks (Quarterly). (n.d.). Retrieved August 10, 2022, from https://ycharts.com/companies/ABT/stock_buyback

ABBOTT VOLUNTARILY RECALLS POWDER FORMULAS MANUFACTURED AT ONE PLANT. (2022, February 17). *Abbott Mediaroom*. Retrieved August 10, 2022, from https://abbott.mediaroom.com/2022-02-17-Abbott-Voluntarily-Recalls-Powder-Formulas-Manufactured-at-One-Plant.

Abolghasemi, H., Hosseini-Divkalayi, N. S., & Seighali, F. (2010). Blood donor incentives: A step forward or backward. Asian journal of transfusion science, 4(1), 9–13. https://doi.org/10.4103/0973-6247.59385

About Us. BIOMILQ. (n.d.). Retrieved September 15, 2022, from https://www.biomilq.com/about

ACNM. (2014). *Delayed umbilical cord clamping - American College of Nurse Midwives*. Retrieved August 17, 2022, from https://www.midwife.org/ACNM/files/ACNMLibraryData/UPLOADFILENAME/000000000290/Delayed-Umbilical-Cord-Clamping-May-2014.pdf

American College of Nurse Midwives (2008). Providing oral nutrition to women in labor. Clinical Bulletin Number 10. Journal of Midwifery & Women's Health, 53, 276–283.

American College of Obstetricians and Gynecologists (2009a). ACOG Committee Opinion No. 441: Oral intake during labor. Obstetrics and Gynecology, 114(3), 714.

American Heart Association. (2021, July 21). *Breastfeeding, even for a few days, linked to lower blood pressure in early childhood*. ScienceDaily. Retrieved August 11, 2022, from https://www.sciencedaily.com/releases/2021/07/210721102422.htm

American Society of Anesthesia (2007). Practice guidelines for obstetric anesthesia: An updated report by the American Society of Anesthesiologists Task Force on Obstetric Anesthesia. Anesthesiology, 106(4), 843–863.

Arnarson, A., & Meeks, S. (2022, March 17). *Folic acid vs. folate - what's the difference?* Healthline. Retrieved August 11, 2022, from https://www.healthline.com/nutrition/folic-acid-vs-folate#vitamin-b-9

Asked what parents should do if they can't find formula, Jen Psaki says call a doctor. Grabien. (n.d.). Retrieved August 31, 2022, from https://grabien.com/story.php?id=378199

Baer, E. (1982, April). *Babies Means Business*. New Internationalist. Retrieved September 19, 2022, from https://newint.org//features/1982/04/01/babies/

Bartick, M., & Reinhold, A. (2010). The burden of suboptimal breastfeeding in the United States: a pediatric cost analysis. Pediatrics, 125(5), e1048–e1056. https://doi.org/10.1542/peds.2009-1616

Baumm, A. (2020, March 10). *Resolution of milk ejection reflex dysfunction & increased breastmilk supply following chiropractic adjustment in a nursing mother of twins: A case report & review of the literature.* Vertebral Subluxation Research. Retrieved August 16, 2022, from https://vertebralsubluxationresearch.com/2020/02/27/resolution-of-milk-ejection-reflex-dysfunction-increased-breastmilk-supply-following-chiropractic-adjustment-in-a-nursing-mother-of-twins-a-case-report-review-of-the-literature/

Bayer. (2022, July 28). *Bayer Provides Update on Path to Closure of Roundup™ Litigation*. Bayer Global. Retrieved September 15, 2022, from https://www.bayer.com/media/en-us/bayer-provides-update-on-path-to-closure-of-rounduptm-litigation/

BBC. (2022, May 9). *US faces Baby Formula 'crisis' as shortage worsens*. BBC News. Retrieved August 10, 2022, from https://www.bbc.com/news/business-61387183

Beach, C. (2022, April 28). *Former employee blows whistle on Baby Formula Production Plant tied to outbreak*. Food Safety News. Retrieved August 10, 2022, from https://www.foodsafetynews.com/2022/04/former-employee-blows-whistle-on-baby-formula-production-plant-tied-to-outbreak/

Beauregard, J. L., Hamner, H. C., Chen, J., Avila-Rodriguez, W., Elam-Evans, L. D., & Perrine, C. G. (2019, August 29). *Racial disparities in breastfeeding initiation and duration among...* Centers for Disease Control and Prevention. Retrieved August 10, 2022, from http://dx.doi.org/10.15585/mmwr.mm6834a3

Belfort, M. B. (2017). *The science of breastfeeding and brain development | breastfeeding medicine*. Breastfeeding Medicine. Retrieved August 12, 2022, from https://www.liebertpub.com/doi/10.1089/bfm.2017.0122

Bever, C. S., Rand, A. A., Nording, M., Taft, D., Kalanetra, K. M., Mills, D. A., Breck, M. A., Smilowitz, J. T., German, J. B., & Hammock, B. D. (2018). Effects of triclosan in breast milk on the infant fecal microbiome. Chemosphere, 203, 467–473. https://doi.org/10.1016/j.chemosphere.2018.03.186

Bittner, G.D., Denison, M.S., Yang, C.Z. et al. Chemicals having estrogenic activity can be released from some bisphenol a-free, hard and clear, thermoplastic resins. Environ Health 13, 103 (2014). https://doi.org/10.1186/1476-069X-13-103

Blesa, M., Sullivan, G., Anblagan, D., Telford, E. J., Quigley, A., Sparrow, S., Serag, A., Semple, S. I., Bastin, M. E., & Boardman, J. P. (n.d.). *Early breast milk exposure modifies brain connectivity in preterm infants*. NeuroImage. Retrieved August 15, 2022, from https://pubmed.ncbi.nlm.nih.gov/30240903/

Bloomberg. (2019, October 2). *Infant Formula Market Size to Reach USD 103.75 Billion by 2026*. Bloomberg.com. Retrieved August 10, 2022, from https://www.bloomberg.com/press-releases/2019-10-02/infant-formula-market-size-to-reach-usd-103-75-billion-by-2026-fortune-business-insights

Body burden: The pollution in newborns. Environmental Working Group. (2005, July 14). Retrieved August 15, 2022, from https://www.ewg.org/research/body-burden-pollution-newborns

Borggren, C. L. (2007, June 20). *Pregnancy and chiropractic: A narrative review of the literature*. Journal of Chiropractic Medicine. Retrieved August 16, 2022, from https://www.sciencedirect.com/science/article/pii/S0899346707000444

Boundy, E. O., Perrine, C. G., Barrera, C. M., Li, R., & Hamner, H. C. (2018). Trends in Maternity Care Practice Skin-to-Skin Contact Indicators: United States, 2007-2015. Breastfeeding medicine : the official journal of the Academy of Breastfeeding Medicine, 13(5), 381–387. https://doi.org/10.1089/bfm.2018.0035

Breastfeeding and Lead Contamination. InfantRisk Center. (2016, March 10). Retrieved August 23, 2022, from https://www.infantrisk.com/breastfeeding-and-lead-contamination

Brown, A., & Lee, M. (2012). Breastfeeding during the first year promotes satiety responsiveness in children aged 18-24 months. Pediatric obesity, 7(5), 382–390. https://doi.org/10.1111/j.2047-6310.2012.00071.x

Burdick, S. (2022, May 16). *White House takes steps to ease infant formula shortage but fails to address industry monopoly.* Children's Health Defense. Retrieved August 10, 2022, from https://childrenshealthdefense.org/defender/baby-formula-shortage-white-house/

Béranger, R., Garlantézec, R., Le Maner-Idrissi, G., Lacroix, A., Rouget, F., Trowbridge, J., Warembourg, C., Monfort, C., Le Gléau, F., Jourdin, M., Multigner, L., Cordier, S., & Chevrier, C. (2017). Prenatal Exposure to Glycol Ethers and Neurocognitive Abilities in 6-Year-Old Children: The PELAGIE Cohort Study. Environmental health perspectives, 125(4), 684–690. https://doi.org/10.1289/EHP39

Cannon, A. M., Kakulas, F., Hepworth, A. R., Lai, C. T., Hartmann, P. E., & Geddes, D. T. (2015). The Effects of Leptin on Breastfeeding Behaviour. International journal of environmental research and public health, 12(10), 12340–12355. https://doi.org/10.3390/ijerph121012340

Center for Food Safety and Applied Nutrition. (2019, September 17). *Abbott Laboratories recalls Calcilo XD® infant formula.* U.S. Food and Drug Administration. Retrieved August 10, 2022, from https://www.fda.gov/safety/recalls-market-withdrawals-safety-alerts/abbott-laboratories-recalls-calcilo-xdr-infant-formula

Center for Food Safety and Applied Nutrition. (2021, February 24). *FDA advises parents and caregivers to not make or feed homemade infant.* U.S. Food and Drug Administration. Retrieved August 10, 2022, from https://www.fda.gov/food/alerts-advisories-safety-information/fda-advises-parents-and-caregivers-not-make-or-feed-homemade-infant-formula-infants

Center for Food Safety and Applied Nutrition. (n.d.). *Investigation of cronobacter infections from powdered infant formula.* U.S. Food and Drug Administration. Retrieved August 10, 2022, from https://www.fda.gov/food/outbreaks-foodborne-illness/fda-investigation-cronobacter-infections-powdered-infant-formula-february-2022?mc_cid=2dec3cdd26

Centers for Disease Control and Prevention (CDC). Cronobacter species isolation in two infants - New Mexico, 2008. MMWR Morb Mortal Wkly Rep. 2009 Oct 30;58(42):1179-83. PMID: 19875980.

Centers for Disease Control and Prevention. (2021, November 24). *Breastfeeding Report Card.* Centers for Disease Control and Prevention. Retrieved August 23, 2022, from https://www.cdc.gov/breastfeeding/data/reportcard.htm

Centers for Disease Control and Prevention. (2022, August 1). *Results: Breastfeeding rates*. Centers for Disease Control and Prevention. Retrieved August 11, 2022, from https://www.cdc.gov/breastfeeding/data/nis_data/results.html

Cesarean Rates. (n.d.). Retrieved September 1, 2022, from https://www.cesareanrates.org/

Chan, M. (2022, May 3). *This startup is creating 'human milk' in a lab*. CNN. Retrieved August 10, 2022, from https://edition.cnn.com/2022/05/03/business/lab-grown-human-milk-biomilq-health-climate-hnk-spc-intl/index.html

Charmatz, H. (2014, May 4). *Can hospitals keep moms and babies together after a cesarean?* SF Birth Doula Heather Charmatz. Retrieved September 1, 2022, from https://sfbirthdoulaandplacentaencapsulationservices.com/birth-blog/2014/5/3/can-hospitals-keep-moms-and-babies-together-after-a-cesarean

Choi, Y. M., Kim, M. K., Kwak, M. K., Kim, D., & Hong, E. G. (2021). Association between thyroid hormones and insulin resistance indices based on the Korean National Health and Nutrition Examination Survey. Scientific reports, 11(1), 21738. https://doi.org/10.1038/s41598-021-01101-z

Clandinin, M. T., Jumpsen, J., & Suh, M. (1994). Relationship between fatty acid accretion, membrane composition, and biologic functions. The Journal of pediatrics, 125(5 Pt 2), S25–S32. https://doi.org/10.1016/s0022-3476(06)80733-x

Cleveland Clinic. (2021, December 22). *Delayed cord clamping: How long, benefits & risks*. Cleveland Clinic. Retrieved August 16, 2022, from https://health.clevelandclinic.org/what-you-should-know-about-delayed-cord-clamping-after-birth/

Cohen, J. (2021, August 1). *U.S. maternal and infant mortality: More signs of public health neglect*. Forbes. Retrieved September 14, 2022, from https://www.forbes.com/sites/joshuacohen/2021/08/01/us-maternal-and-infant-mortality-more-signs-of-public-health-neglect/?sh=1f499223a508

Commissioner, O. of the. (2022, March 28). *FDA seeks $8.4 billion to further investments in critical public health modernization, Core Food and medical product safety programs*. FDA NEWS RELEASE. Retrieved September 8, 2022, from https://www.fda.gov/news-events/press-announcements/fda-seeks-84-billion-further-investments-critical-public-health-modernization-core-food-and-medical

CONFIDENTIAL DISCLOSURE RE ABBOTT LABORATORIES' PRODUCTION SITE IN STURGIS, MICHIGAN. DocumentCloud. (2021, October 19). Retrieved August 10, 2022, from https://www.documentcloud.org/documents/22051317-confidential-disclosure-re-abbott-laboratories-production-site-in-sturgis-michigan

Dada Su, Maria Pasalich, Andy H Lee, Colin W Binns, Ovarian cancer risk is reduced by prolonged lactation: a case-control study in southern China, The American Journal of Clinical Nutrition, Volume 97, Issue 2, February 2013, Pages 354–359, https://doi.org/10.3945/ajcn.112.044719

Declercq E., Sakala C., Corry M., Applebaum S., Herrlich A. (2013). Listening to mothers III: Pregnancy and childbirth. New York, NY: Childbirth Connection.

Downey, K. (2020, April 8). *AAP recommends temporarily separating newborns from mothers with covid-19*. Healio. Retrieved August 11, 2022, from https://www.healio.com/news/pediatrics/20200408/aap-recommends-temporarily-separating-newborns-from-mothers-with-covid19

Downey, K. (2020, July 28). *Aap no longer recommends separating newborns from mothers with covid-19*. Healio. Retrieved August 11, 2022, from https://www.healio.com/news/pediatrics/20200728/aap-no-longer-recommends-separating-newborns-from-mothers-with-covid19

Economic Research Service, Oliveira, V., Prell, M., Smallwood, D., & Frazao, E., WIC and the Retail Price of Infant Formula (2004). United States Department of Agriculture. Retrieved August 21, 2022, from https://www.ers.usda.gov/webdocs/publications/46787/15976_fanrr39-1_1_.pdf?v=0.

Editor. (2022, June 8). *Chiropractic care during pregnancy*. American Pregnancy Association. Retrieved August 16, 2022, from https://americanpregnancy.org/healthy-pregnancy/pregnancy-health-wellness/chiropractic-care-during-pregnancy/

Edney, A. (2022, May 12). Bloomberg.com. Retrieved August 10, 2022, from https://www.bloomberg.com/news/articles/2022-05-12/inspectors-saw-bacteria-risk-at-abbott-formula-factory-last-year

The Endocrine Society. (2009, June 12). Bisphenol A Exposure In Pregnant Mice Permanently Changes DNA Of Offspring. ScienceDaily. Retrieved August 14, 2022 from www.sciencedaily.com/releases/2009/06/090610124428.htm

Fallon J.M. Chiropractic and pregnancy: a partnership for the future. ICA Int Rev Chiropr. 1990;46(6):39–42.

FAO/WHO [Food and Agriculture Organization of the United Nations/World Health Organization]. 2008. Enterobacter sakazakii (Cronobacter spp.) in powdered follow-up formulae. Microbiological Risk Assessment Series No. 15. Rome. 90pp.

FDA. (n.d.). *FDA warns consumers not to use certain powdered infant formula produced in Abbott Nutrition's facility in Sturgis, Michigan.* U.S. Food and Drug Administration. Retrieved August 10, 2022, from https://www.fda.gov/news-events/press-announcements/fda-warns-consumers-not-use-certain-powdered-infant-formula-produced-abbott-nutritions-facility

Food and Drug Administration, & Hathaway, T.J., Form FDA 4831–9 (n.d.). Inspectional Observations.

Food and Drug Administration. (2022, April 13). *Threshold of regulation (TOR) exemptions.* Threshold of Regulation (TOR) Exemptions. Retrieved August 22, 2022, from https://www.cfsanappsexternal.fda.gov/scripts/fdcc/index.cfm?set=TOR&id=2005-006&sort=File&order=DESC&startrow=1&type=basic&search=perchlorate

Gasparro, A., & Kang, J. (2022, May 13). *Baby formula shortage could leave parents scrambling for months.* The Wall Street Journal. Retrieved August 10, 2022, from https://www.wsj.com/articles/baby-formula-shortage-could-last-months-11652371827?mod=hp_lead_pos3%2F

Geier, D. A., Hooker, B. S., Kern, J. K., King, P. G., Sykes, L. K., & Geier, M. R. (2014). A dose-response relationship between organic mercury exposure from thimerosal-containing vaccines and neurodevelopmental disorders. International journal of environmental research and public health, 11(9), 9156–9170. https://doi.org/10.3390/ijerph110909156

Gillam, C. (2015, April 17). *U.S. regulators may recommend testing food for glyphosate residues.* Reuters. Retrieved August 10, 2022, from https://www.reuters.com/article/us-food-agriculture-glyphosate/u-s-regulators-may-recommend-testing-food-for-glyphosate-residues-idUSKBN0N82K020150417

Goer H., Romano A. (2012). Optimal care in childbirth: The case for a physiologic approach. Seattle, WA: Classic Day.

Gonen, R., Korobochka, R., Degani, S., & Gaitini, L. (2000). Association between epidural analgesia and intrapartum fever. American journal of perinatology, 17(3), 127–130. https://doi.org/10.1055/s-2000-9283

Goodin, E. (2022, May 12). 'Babies Died': Jen Psaki Defends the Government's Closure of Abbott Plant. Daily Mail Online. Retrieved August 31, 2022, from https://www.dailymail.co.uk/news/article-10811079/Babies-died-Jen-Psaki-DEFENDS-governments-closure-Abbott-plant.html

Gouchon, S., Gregori, D., Picotto, A., Patrucco, G., Nangeroni, M., & Di Giulio, P. (2010). Skin-to-skin contact after cesarean delivery: an experimental study. Nursing research, 59(2), 78–84. https://doi.org/10.1097/NNR.0b013e3181d1a8bc

Grey, H. (2018, January 4). Breast Milk Banks: Should women be paid? Healthline. Retrieved September 8, 2022, from https://www.healthline.com/health-news/compensation-for-donating-breast-milk

Grube MM, von der Lippe E, Schlaud M, Brettschneider A-K (2015) Does Breastfeeding Help to Reduce the Risk of Childhood Overweight and Obesity? A Propensity Score Analysis of Data from the KiGGS Study. PLoS ONE 10(3): e0122534. doi:10.1371/journal.pone.0122534

Gunderson EP, Hurston SR, Ning X, Lo JC, Crites Y, Walton D, Dewey KG, Azevedo RA, Young S, Fox G, Elmasian CC, Salvador N, Lum M, Sternfeld B, Quesenberry CP Jr; Study of Women, Infant Feeding and Type 2 Diabetes After GDM Pregnancy Investigators. Lactation and Progression to Type 2 Diabetes Mellitus After Gestational Diabetes Mellitus: A Prospective Cohort Study. Ann Intern Med. 2015 Dec 15;163(12):889-98. doi: 10.7326/M15-0807. Epub 2015 Nov 24. PMID: 26595611; PMCID: PMC5193135.

Guomao Zheng, Erika Schreder, Jennifer C. Dempsey, Nancy Uding, Valerie Chu, Gabriel Andres, Sheela Sathyanarayana, and Amina Salamova Environmental Science & Technology 2021 55 (11), 7510-7520 DOI: 10.1021/acs.est.0c06978

Guyton KZ, Loomis D, Grosse Y, El Ghissassi F, Benbrahim-Tallaa L, Guha N, Scoccianti C, Mattock H, Straif K, International Agency for Research on Cancer Monograph Working Group ILF. Carcinogenicity of tetrachlorvinphos, parathion, malathion, diazinon, and glyphosate. Lancet Oncol. 2015;16:490-491.

Hamdan A, Tamim H. The relationship between postpartum depression and breastfeeding. Int J Psychiatry Med. 2012;43(3):243-59. doi: 10.2190/PM.43.3.d. PMID: 22978082.

HarperCollinsPublishers.(n.d.).*TheAmericanHeritageDictionaryEntry:Intervention*. American Heritage Dictionary Entry: intervention. Retrieved August 16, 2022, from https://ahdictionary.com/word/search.html?q=intervention

Hauck FR, Thompson JM, Tanabe KO, Moon RY, Vennemann MM. Breastfeeding and reduced risk of sudden infant death syndrome: a meta-analysis. Pediatrics. 2011 Jul;128(1):103-10. doi: 10.1542/peds.2010-3000. Epub 2011 Jun 13. PMID: 21669892.

Heise, A. M., & Wiessinger, D. (2011). Dysphoric milk ejection reflex: A case report. International breastfeeding journal, 6(1), 6. https://doi.org/10.1186/1746-4358-6-6

Hengstermann, S., Mantaring, J. B. V., Sobel, H. L., Borja, V. E., Basilio, J., Iellamo, A. D., & Nyunt-U, S. (2009, September 16). *Formula feeding is associated with increased hospital admissions due to...* Journal of Human Lactation. Retrieved August 11, 2022, from https://journals.sagepub.com/doi/10.1177/0890334409344078

Hofmeyr, G. J., Mshweshwe, N. T., & Gülmezoglu, A. M. (2015). Controlled cord traction for the third stage of labour. The Cochrane database of systematic reviews, 1(1), CD008020. https://doi.org/10.1002/14651858.CD008020.pub2

Hofvander Y. (2005). Breastfeeding and the Baby Friendly Hospitals Initiative (BFHI): organization, response and outcome in Sweden and other countries. Acta paediatrica (Oslo, Norway : 1992), 94(8), 1012–1016. https://doi.org/10.1111/j.1651-2227.2005.tb02038.x

Houlihan, J., & Brody, C. (2019, October). *What's in my baby's food?* Healthy Babies Bright Futures. Retrieved August 21, 2022, from https://www.healthybabyfood.org/sites/healthybabyfoods.org/files/2019-10/BabyFoodReport_FULLREPORT_ENGLISH_R5b.pdf

Iversen, C., A. Lehner, N. Mullane, E. Bidlas, I. Cleenwerck, J. Marugg, S. Fanning, R. Stephan, and H. Joosten. 2007. "The taxonomy of Enterobacter sakazakii: proposal of a new genus Cronobacter", 1. BMC Evol. Biol. 7:64.

Iversen, C., Mullane, N., McCardell, B., Tall, B. D., Lehner, A., Fanning, S., Stephan, R., & Joosten, H. (2008, June 1). *Cronobacter gen. nov., a new genus to accommodate the biogroups of Enterobacter sakazakii...* International Journal of Systematic and Evolutionary Microbiology. Retrieved August 10, 2022, from https://doi.org/10.1099%2Fijs.0.65577-0

Jacknowitz, A., Novillo, D., & Tiehen, L. (2007, February 1). *Special Supplemental Nutrition Program for Women, infants, and children and infant feeding practices.* American Academy of Pediatrics. Retrieved August 15, 2022, from https://publications.aap.org/pediatrics/article-abstract/119/2/281/70305/Special-Supplemental-Nutrition-Program-for-Women

Jennifer Shutt, L. I. M. 17. (2022, May 17). *U.S. House to vote on $28 million for FDA to relieve infant formula shortage*. Louisiana Illuminator. Retrieved August 10, 2022, from https://lailluminator.com/2022/05/17/u-s-house-to-vote-on-28-million-for-fda-to-relieve-infant-formula-shortage/

Justice Department files complaint and proposed consent decree to ensure safety of Abbott Laboratories' infant formula. The United States Department of Justice. (2022, May 16). Retrieved August 10, 2022, from https://www.justice.gov/Usao-wdmi/pr/2022_0516_Abbott

Knight, S. (2022, May 17). *Company responsible for Tainted Baby Formula Has Monopoly Over Aid Program sales*. Company Responsible for Tainted Baby Formula Has Monopoly Over Aid Program Sales. Retrieved August 10, 2022, from https://truthout.org/articles/company-responsible-for-tainted-baby-formula-has-monopoly-over-aid-program-sales/

Korbatov, A. B., & De Souza, R.-M. (2015, November 19). *What explains the United States' dismal maternal mortality rates?* Wilson Center. Retrieved September 27, 2022, from https://www.wilsoncenter.org/event/what-explains-the-united-states-dismal-maternal-mortality-rates

Kozhimannil, K. B., Xu, X., & Glance, L. G. (2013, March 1). *Cesarean delivery rates vary tenfold among us hospitals; reducing variation may address quality and cost issues: Health Affairs Journal*. Health Affairs. Retrieved September 1, 2022, from https://www.healthaffairs.org/doi/10.1377/hlthaff.2012.1030

Kramer, M. S., Aboud, F., Mironova, E., Vanilovich, I., Platt, R. W., Matush, L., Igumnov, S., Fombonne, E., Bogdanovich, N., Ducruet, T., Collet, J. P., Chalmers, B., Hodnett, E., Davidovsky, S., Skugarevsky, O., Trofimovich, O., Kozlova, L., Shapiro, S., & Promotion of Breastfeeding Intervention Trial (PROBIT) Study Group (2008). Breastfeeding and child cognitive development: new evidence from a large randomized trial. Archives of general psychiatry, 65(5), 578–584. https://doi.org/10.1001/archpsyc.65.5.578

Kujawa-Myles, S., Noel-Weiss, J., Dunn, S., Peterson, W. E., & Cotterman, K. J. (2015). Maternal intravenous fluids and postpartum breast changes: a pilot observational study. International breastfeeding journal, 10, 18. https://doi.org/10.1186/s13006-015-0043-8

Lee, H., Park, H., Ha, E., Hong, Y. C., Ha, M., Park, H., Kim, B. N., Lee, B., Lee, S. J., Lee, K. Y., Kim, J. H., Jeong, K. S., & Kim, Y. (2016). Effect of Breastfeeding Duration on Cognitive Development in Infants: 3-Year Follow-up Study. Journal of Korean medical science, 31(4), 579–584. https://doi.org/10.3346/jkms.2016.31.4.579

Li, R., Dee, D., Li, C. M., Hoffman, H. J., & Grummer-Strawn, L. M. (2014). Breastfeeding and risk of infections at 6 years. Pediatrics, 134 Suppl 1(Suppl 1), S13–S20. https://doi.org/10.1542/peds.2014-0646D

Li, R., Fein, S. B., Chen, J., & Grummer-Strawn, L. M. (2008, October). *Why mothers stop breastfeeding: Mothers' self-reported reasons for stopping during the first year*. Pediatrics. Retrieved August 11, 2022, from https://pubmed.ncbi.nlm.nih.gov/18829834/

Low blood sugar in the newborn baby. International BreastFeeding Centre. (2009, July). Retrieved August 11, 2022, from https://ibconline.ca/information-sheets/hypoglycaemia-of-the-newborn-low-blood-sugar/

Malloy, M. H., Graubard, B., Moss, H., McCarthy, M., Gwyn, S., Vietze, P., Willoughby, A., Rhoads, G. G., & Berendes, H. (1991). Hypochloremic metabolic alkalosis from ingestion of a chloride-deficient infant formula: outcome 9 and 10 years later. Pediatrics, 87(6), 811–822.

Marowitz A. (2014). Caring for women in early labor: can we delay admission and meet women's needs?. Journal of midwifery & women's health, 59(6), 645–650. https://doi.org/10.1111/jmwh.12252

Mata Jiménez, L., Sáenz, P., Araya, J. R., Allen, M. de los Á., García, M. E., & Carvajal, J. J. (1988, September 1). *Promotion of Breastfeeding in Costa Rica: the Puriscal study*. Repositorio Institucional de la Universidad de Costa Rica. Retrieved September 19, 2022, from https://www.kerwa.ucr.ac.cr/handle/10669/15562

McCoy, M. B., & Heggie, P. (2020, July 1). *In-hospital formula feeding and breastfeeding duration*. American Academy of Pediatrics. Retrieved August 15, 2022, from https://doi.org/10.1542/peds.2019-2946

Mercola, J. (2022, May 8). The Stunning Health Benefits of Sauna Therapy [web log]. Retrieved August 16, 2022.

Merriam-Webster. (n.d.). *Starve Definition & Meaning*. Merriam-Webster. Retrieved August 10, 2022, from https://www.merriam-webster.com/dictionary/starve

Mills PJ, Kania-Korwel I, Fagan J, McEvoy LK, Laughlin GA, Barrett-Connor E. Excretion of the Herbicide Glyphosate in Older Adults Between 1993 and 2016. JAMA. 2017;318(16):1610–1611. doi:10.1001/jama.2017.11726

Milman, O. (2019, May 22). *US cosmetics are full of chemicals banned by Europe – why?* The Guardian. Retrieved August 15, 2022, from https://www.theguardian.com/us-news/2019/may/22/chemicals-in-cosmetics-us-restricted-eu

Minckas, N., Medvedev, M. M., Adejuyigbe, E. A., Brotherton, H., Chellani, H., & Estifanos, E. S. (2021, February 15). *Preterm care during the COVID-19 pandemic: A comparative risk analysis of neonatal deaths averted by kangaroo mother care versus mortality due to SARS-CoV-2 infection.* eClinicalMedicine. Retrieved August 11, 2022, from https://www.thelancet.com/journals/eclinm/article/PIIS2589-5370(21)00013-4/fulltext

Moore, E. R., Anderson, G. C., Bergman, N., & Dowswell, T. (2012). Early skin-to-skin contact for mothers and their healthy newborn infants. The Cochrane database of systematic reviews, 5(5), CD003519. https://doi.org/10.1002/14651858.CD003519.pub3

Muller, M. (1974). *The Baby Killer*. London; War on Want.

New research highlights risks of separating newborns from mothers during COVID-19 pandemic. (2021, March 16). *World Health Organization*. Retrieved August 11, 2022, from https://www.who.int/news/item/16-03-2021-new-research-highlights-risks-of-separating-newborns-from-mothers-during-covid-19-pandemic.

The New York Times. (1981, October 27). *Study on infant formula use*. The New York Times. Retrieved September 19, 2022, from https://www.nytimes.com/1981/10/27/style/study-on-infant-formula-use.html

NHS. (2012, November 20). *Infant Feeding Survey 2010 Consolidated Report*. NHS choices. Retrieved August 11, 2022, from https://digital.nhs.uk/data-and-information/publications/statistical/infant-feeding-survey/infant-feeding-survey-uk-2010#key-facts

Nielsen, C., Li, Y., Lewandowski, M., Fletcher, T., & Jakobsson, K. (2022). Breastfeeding initiation and duration after high exposure to perfluoroalkyl substances through contaminated drinking water: A cohort study from Ronneby, Sweden. Environmental research, 207, 112206. https://doi.org/10.1016/j.envres.2021.112206

Oliveira, V. (2011, September 11). *Winner takes (almost) all: How WIC affects the infant formula market*. USDA ERS - Infant Formula Market. Retrieved September 8, 2022, from https://www.ers.usda.gov/amber-waves/2011/september/infant-formula-market/

Osterman , M. J. K., Hamilton, B. E., Martin, J. A., Driscoll, A. K., & Valenzuela, C. P. (2022, February 7). *National Vital Statistics reports - Centers for Disease Control and ...* https://www.cdc.gov/nchs/products/index.htm. Retrieved August 9, 2022, from https://www.cdc.gov/nchs/data/nvsr/nvsr70/NVSR70-17.pdf

Our science. BIOMILQ. (n.d.). Retrieved August 10, 2022, from https://www.biomilq.com/our-science

Overstreet, R. M. (1938). The Increase of Scurvy. *Northwest Medicine*.

Parvez, S., Gerona, R.R., Proctor, C. et al. Glyphosate exposure in pregnancy and shortened gestational length: a prospective Indiana birth cohort study. Environ Health 17, 23 (2018). https://doi.org/10.1186/s12940-018-0367-0

Patel AL, Kim JH. Human milk and necrotizing enterocolitis. Semin Pediatr Surg. 2018 Feb;27(1):34-38. doi: 10.1053/j.sempedsurg.2017.11.007. Epub 2017 Nov 6. PMID: 29275815.

Pavlich, K. (2022, May 11). *Biden's incoming press secretary laughs when asked who is handling baby formula crisis*. Townhall. Retrieved August 31, 2022, from https://townhall.com/tipsheet/katiepavlich/2022/05/11/bidens-incoming-press-secretary-laughs-about-baby-formula-shortage-n2607079

Pearson, C. (2020, July 30). *The pressure to breastfeed can hurt women. and doctors are finally realizing it*. HuffPost. Retrieved August 21, 2022, from https://www.huffpost.com/entry/breastfeeding-pressure-women-mental-health-doctor_l_5d811672e4b00d69059fc2d0

Pejovic, N. J., & Herlenius, E. (2013). Unexpected collapse of healthy newborn infants: risk factors, supervision and hypothermia treatment. Acta paediatrica (Oslo, Norway : 1992), 102(7), 680–688. https://doi.org/10.1111/apa.12244

Pereira, A., Cruz-Melguizo, S., Adrien, M. et al. Breastfeeding mothers with COVID-19 infection: a case series. Int Breastfeed J 15, 69 (2020). https://doi.org/10.1186/s13006-020-00314-8

Prell, M. (2004, December). *An Economic Model of WIC, the Infant Formula Rebate Program, and the Retail Price of Infant Formula*. Food Assistance and Nutrition

Research Report Number 39-2. Retrieved August 15, 2022, from https://www.ers.usda.gov/publications

Preston, E. V., Fruh, V., Quinn, M. R., Hacker, M. R., Wylie, B. J., O'Brien, K., Mahalingaiah, S., & James-Todd, T. (2021). Endocrine disrupting chemical-associated hair product use during pregnancy and gestational age at delivery: a pilot study. Environmental health : a global access science source, 20(1), 86. https://doi.org/10.1186/s12940-021-00772-5

Redly, M. (2001). *The effects of chiropractic care on a patient with chronic constipation.* Journal of Canadian Chiropractic Association. Retrieved August 16, 2022, from https://www.chiropractic.ca/wp-content/uploads/2014/07/Pages185-191.pdf

Rehfeld, A., Egeberg, D. L., Almstrup, K., Petersen, J. H., Dissing, S., & Skakkebæk, N. E. (2018). EDC IMPACT: Chemical UV filters can affect human sperm function in a progesterone-like manner. Endocrine connections, 7(1), 16–25. https://doi.org/10.1530/EC-17-0156

Rodriguez, N. A., Hageman, J. R., & Pellerite, M. (2018, May 18). *Maternal distraction from smartphone use: a potential risk factor for sudden unexpected postnatal collapse of the newborn.* Retrieved September 1, 2022, from https://doi.org/10.1016/j.jpeds.2018.04.031

Rodríguez-Carmona, Y., Cantoral, A., Trejo-Valdivia, B., Téllez-Rojo, M. M., Svensson, K., Peterson, K. E., Meeker, J. D., Schnaas, L., Solano, M., & Watkins, D. J. (2019). Phthalate exposure during pregnancy and long-term weight gain in women. Environmental research, 169, 26–32. https://doi.org/10.1016/j.envres.2018.10.014

Rothwell, C. (2019, August 14). *AAP's relationship with Formula companies.* USLCA. Retrieved August 23, 2022, from https://uslca.org/clinical-pearl/aap-and-formula-companies/

Roy, A. (2020, June 16). *Bill Gates' climate-change investment firm bets on lab-produced breast milk.* CNBC. Retrieved August 10, 2022, from https://www.cnbc.com/2020/06/16/biomilq-raises-3point5-million-from-bill-gates-investment-firm.html

Rupp, L. (2021, October 28). *Paid maternity leave by country: Only 5 places are as stingy as U.S.* Bloomberg.com. Retrieved September 2, 2022, from https://www.bloomberg.com/news/articles/2021-10-28/paid-family-leave-how-much-does-us-offer-compared-to-other-countries

Rupp, L. (2021, October 28). *Paid maternity leave by country: Only 5 places are as stingy as U.S.* Bloomberg.com. Retrieved September 2, 2022, from https://www.bloomberg.com/news/articles/2021-10-28/paid-family-leave-how-much-does-us-offer-compared-to-other-countries

Rupp, L. (2021, October 28). *Paid maternity leave by country: Only 5 places are as stingy as U.S.* Bloomberg.com. Retrieved September 20, 2022, from https://www.bloomberg.com/news/articles/2021-10-28/paid-family-leave-how-much-does-us-offer-compared-to-other-countries?leadSource=uverify+wall

Sadauskaite-Kuehne V, Ludvigsson J, Padaiga Z, Jasinskiene E, Samuelsson U. Longer breastfeeding is an independent protective factor against development of type 1 diabetes mellitus in childhood. Diabetes Metab Res Rev. 2004 Mar-Apr;20(2):150-7. doi: 10.1002/dmrr.425. PMID: 15037991.

Sakai-Bizmark R, Ross MG, Estevez D, Bedel LEM, Marr EH, Tsugawa Y. Evaluation of Hospital Cesarean Delivery–Related Profits and Rates in the United States. JAMA Netw Open. 2021;4(3):e212235. doi:10.1001/jamanetworkopen.2021.2235

Sarah A. Keim, Manjusha M. Kulkarni, Kelly McNamara, Sheela R. Geraghty, Rachael M. Billock, Rachel Ronau, Joseph S. Hogan, Jesse J. Kwiek; Cow's Milk Contamination of Human Milk Purchased via the Internet. Pediatrics May 2015; 135 (5): e1157–e1162. 10.1542/peds.2014-3554

Sarantis, H., Naidenko, O. V., Gray, S., Houlihan, J., & Malkan, S. (2010, May 12). *Not so Sexy - Environmental Working Group.* The Health Risks of Secret Chemicals in Fragrance. Retrieved August 16, 2022, from https://www.ewg.org/sites/default/files/report/SafeCosmetics_FragranceRpt.pdf

Sartwelle T. (2012). Electronic fetal monitoring: A bridge too far. Journal of Legal Medicine, 33, 313–379.

Sears, M. E., Kerr, K. J., & Bray, R. I. (2012). Arsenic, cadmium, lead, and mercury in sweat: a systematic review. Journal of environmental and public health, 2012, 184745. https://doi.org/10.1155/2012/184745

Selby, G. (2021, April 27). *Future of milk: Singapore start-up TurtleTree expands to us to leverage food tech growth.* Food Ingredients First. Retrieved August 10, 2022, from https://www.foodingredientsfirst.com/news/future-of-milk-singapore-start-up-turtletree-expands-to-us-to-leverage-food-tech-growth.html

Shea, D. (2022, April 28). *Who reveals shocking extent of exploitative formula milk marketing.* Univadis. Retrieved August 10, 2022, from https://www.univadis.

it/viewarticle/who-reveals-shocking-extent-of-exploitative-formula-milk-marketing-764711

Smyth R., Markham C., Dowswell T. (2013). Amniotomy for shortening spontaneous labour. Cochrane Database of Systematic Reviews, (6), CD006167. 10.1002/14651858.CD006167.pub4 Retrieved from http://onlinelibrary.wiley.com/doi/10.1002/14651858.CD006167.pub4/full

Solomon, S. (1981, December 6). *The Controversy Over Infant Formula*. Retrieved September 19, 2022, from https://www.nytimes.com/1981/12/06/magazine/the-controversy-over-infant-formula.html?pagewanted=all

Sousa, R. (2021, October 21). *Biomilq secures $21M in series A funding round*. FoodBev Media. Retrieved August 10, 2022, from https://www.foodbev.com/news/biomilq-secures-21m-in-series-a-funding-round/

Strickland, L. (2021, October 19). *Happy birthday BIOMILQ: A reflection by Leila Strickland, our CSO & Co-founder*. BIOMILQ. Retrieved September 20, 2022, from https://www.biomilq.com/post/happy-birthday-biomilq-a-reflection-by-leila-strickland-our-cso-co-founder

Strysko, J., Cope, J. R., Martin, H., Tarr, C., Hise, K., Collier, S., & Bowen, A. (2020, May). *Food safety and invasive cronobacter infections during early infancy, 1961–2018*. Emerging Infectious Diseases journal. Retrieved August 10, 2022, from https://doi.org/10.3201/eid2605.190858

Stuebe A. (2009). The risks of not breastfeeding for mothers and infants. Reviews in obstetrics & gynecology, 2(4), 222–231.

Stuebe A. (2020). Should Infants Be Separated from Mothers with COVID-19? First, Do No Harm. Breastfeeding medicine : the official journal of the Academy of Breastfeeding Medicine, 15(5), 351–352. https://doi.org/10.1089/bfm.2020.29153.ams

Swenson, K., & Portnoy, J. (2022, May 13). *U.S. baby formula shortage leaves parents scrambling*. The Washington Post. Retrieved August 21, 2022, from https://www.washingtonpost.com/dc-md-va/2022/05/11/formula-shortage-parents-inflation/

Szalinski, C. (19AD). *A very expensive, technically illegal workaround to the formula shortage*. The Atlantic. Retrieved August 18, 2022, from https://www.msn.com/en-us/news/us/rich-parents-are-tapping-into-a-baby-formula-black-market/ar-AAXtJed

Thakrar, A. P., Forrest, A. D., Maltenfort, M. G., & Forrest, C. B. (2018, January 1). *Child mortality in the US and 19 OECD comparator nations: A 50-year time-trend analysis: Health Affairs Journal*. Health Affairs. Retrieved August 10, 2022, from https://www.healthaffairs.org/doi/10.1377/hlthaff.2017.0767

Tomey, R. (2022, May 30). *FDA, Abbott Labs both to blame for the ongoing Baby Formula Shortage*. Newstarget.com. Retrieved August 10, 2022, from https://newstarget.com/2022-05-30-fda-abbott-share-blame-baby-formula-shortage.html

Tulleken, C. van, Wright, C., Brown, A., McCoy, D., & Costello, A. (2020, October 24). *Marketing of Breastmilk Substitutes During the COVID-19 Pandemic*. https://doi.org/10.1016/S0140-6736(20)32119-X. Retrieved August 10, 2022, from https://www.thelancet.com/journals/lancet/article/PIIS0140-6736(20)32119-X/fulltext

U.S. Department of Health and Human Services. (2021, November). *Bisphenol A (BPA)*. National Institute of Environmental Health Sciences. Retrieved August 15, 2022, from https://www.niehs.nih.gov/health/topics/agents/sya-bpa/index.cfm

U.S. Department of Health and Human Services. (2022, July 11). *Preterm birth more likely with exposure to phthalates*. National Institutes of Health. Retrieved August 22, 2022, from https://www.nih.gov/news-events/news-releases/preterm-birth-more-likely-exposure-phthalates

van den Elsen, L., Garssen, J., Burcelin, R., & Verhasselt, V. (2019). Shaping the Gut Microbiota by Breastfeeding: The Gateway to Allergy Prevention?. Frontiers in pediatrics, 7, 47. https://doi.org/10.3389/fped.2019.00047

Vorderstrasse, B. A., Fenton, S. E., Bohn, A. A., Cundiff, J. A., & Lawrence, B. P. (2004). A novel effect of dioxin: exposure during pregnancy severely impairs mammary gland differentiation. Toxicological sciences : an official journal of the Society of Toxicology, 78(2), 248–257. https://doi.org/10.1093/toxsci/kfh062

Wasson, E. (2021, October 27). *Democrats abandon paid family leave from Biden Economic Plan*. Bloomberg Law. Retrieved September 20, 2022, from https://news.bloomberglaw.com/daily-labor-report/democrats-drop-paid-family-leave-from-biden-economic-plan

When pregnancy goes past your due date. The American College of Obstetricians and Gynecology. (n.d.). Retrieved August 16, 2022, from https://www.acog.org/womens-health/faqs/when-pregnancy-goes-past-your-due-date

WHO. Guideline: Delayed umbilical cord clamping for improved maternal and infant health and nutrition outcomes. Geneva: World Health Organization; 2014.

WHO. UNICEF. IBFAN. Marketing of Breast-milk Substitutes: National Implementation of the International Code. Status Report 2016. Geneva: World Health Organization; 2016.

WIC Data Tables. Food and Nutrition Service U.S. Department of Agriculture. (2022, July 8). Retrieved August 10, 2022, from https://www.fns.usda.gov/pd/wic-program

Widström, A. M., Lilja, G., Aaltomaa-Michalias, P., Dahlöf, A., Lintula, M., & Nissen, E. (2011). Newborn behaviour to locate the breast when skin-to-skin: a possible method for enabling early self-regulation. Acta paediatrica (Oslo, Norway : 1992), 100(1), 79–85. https://doi.org/10.1111/j.1651-2227.2010.01983.x

Wolf, J. H. (2011, October 10). *Low breastfeeding rates and public health in the United States.* American Journal of Public Health. Retrieved August 10, 2022, from https://ajph.aphapublications.org/doi/full/10.2105/AJPH.93.12.2000

World Health Organization (1996). Care in normal birth: A practical guide. Geneva, Switzerland: Author; Retrieved from http://whqlibdoc.who.int/hq/1996/WHO_FRH_MSM_96.24.pdf

World Health Organization, United Nations Children's Fund. Guideline: updates on HIV and infant feeding: the duration of breastfeeding, and support from health services to improve feeding practices among mothers living with HIV. Geneva: World Health Organization; 2016.

World Health Organization. (2020, March 13). *Clinical management of severe acute respiratory infection (SARI) when covid-19 disease is suspected: Interim guidance, 13 March 2020.* World Health Organization. Retrieved August 18, 2022, from https://www.who.int/europe/publications/i/item/WHO-2019-nCoV-clinical-2020-4

Xu L, Lochhead P, Ko Y, Claggett B, Leong RW, Ananthakrishnan AN. Systematic review with meta-analysis: breastfeeding and the risk of Crohn's disease and ulcerative colitis. Aliment Pharmacol Ther. 2017 Nov;46(9):780-789. doi: 10.1111/apt.14291. Epub 2017 Sep 11. PMID: 28892171; PMCID: PMC5688338.

Zheng, G., Schreder, E., Dempsey, J. C., Uding, N., Chu, V., Andres, G., Sathyanarayana, S., & Salamova, A. (2021, April 25). *Per- and Polyfluoroalkyl Substances (PFAS) in Breast Milk: Concerning Trends for Current-Use PFAS.* Cen.acs.org. Retrieved August 18, 2022, from https://cen.acs.org/environment/persistent-pollutants/PFAS-pervade-breast-milk/99/i19

Thank you for reading Starving Babies. This book has a companion website with additional resources (Like the endocrine action plan, Connected Birth Mapping, and the Parachute Plan mentioned herein). Links to research, blog updates, and helpful products or collaborating organizations and websites, as well as opportunities to join the Starving Babies community can all be accessed at starvingbabies.com. The author also conducts live seminars and speaking engagements and would welcome inquiries for opportunities to speak with your organization. A portion of these proceeds are donated back to the local community and local birth and breastfeeding support resources. Please email info@starvingbabies.com for more information.

Made in the USA
Monee, IL
10 November 2023